Weisman ok @

Dietrich

Long
10k
0743

DOCTORS EAST
DOCTORS WEST

Bringing a Little Patient to the Hospital

DOCTORS EAST
DOCTORS WEST

An American Physician's
Life in China

By EDWARD H. HUME, M.D.

The way is one, the winds blow together.

W · W · NORTON & COMPANY · INC · New York

AFFECTIONATELY DEDICATED

TO MY WIFE

LOTTA

AND TO MY THREE CHILDREN

THEODORE, CHARLOTTE, JOY

WHO SHARED SO FULLY IN THE LIFE EXPERIENCE

CONTENTS

7

8 CONTENTS

ILLUSTRATIONS

ACKNOWLEDGMENT

GRATEFUL acknowledgment is made to all those colleagues, doctors and nurses, as well as architects, secretaries, and business staff, who took part, with such complete devotion, in laying the foundations of the Hsiangya enterprise. My academic colleagues, too, rendered invaluable service as they worked with our medical group on the original Hsiangya board and aided in its effective functioning. Without the co-operation of all these friends, the advancement of the Hsiangya medical plans would scarcely have been possible.

In the years before the Revolution, there were four active medical colleagues: Helen Howe Gage, M.D., Nina D. Gage, R.N., Kung-hsiao Hou, M.D., and Fu-ch'ing Yen, M.D. The number grew rapidly after the Hsiangya Medical College started in 1913–14. They are now too many to name one by one, but their record of service abides, inscribed indelibly on the structure of modern medicine in China.

I wish to thank Dr. Hu Shih, former ambassador of the Chinese Republic to Washington, for consenting to write the characters reproduced on the title page; as well as Dr. C. T. Tsu and Dr. H. P. Yang of the China Institute for their help in writing the characters at the head of the chapters. Four other scholars have given invaluable historical aid: Dr. A. Kaiming Ch'iu, Librarian of the Harvard-Yenching Institute, Cambridge; Professor L. Carrington Goodrich, head of the Chinese department, Columbia University; Professor Arthur W. Hummel, director of the Division of Orientalia, Library

11

of Congress; Mr. C. Meng, director of the China Institute of America. My gratitude to them is real.

I am grateful to the following organizations for the privilege of reproducing the pictures listed below:

(1) Chinese News Service, for photographs by George Alexanderson, U. S. Department of State, technical photographic adviser to the Ministry of Information, Chungking: Ricefields Stretching into the Distance; The Powerful Water Buffalo; Right among Shopkeepers for Neighbors; The Sweetmeat Vendor; The Peddler of Chinaware; One of the Nursing Pioneers; Dr. Wang, My Medical Consultant; The Hospital Ricksha Man; Hsiangya Unit at the Fighting Front.

(2) United China Relief, for the photograph entitled "Little Basket Boy."

(3) Black Star, for the frontispiece photograph.

PROLOGUE

FROM THE earliest days, men of medicine have journeyed ceaselessly to learn of the progress other physicians have made. They have disdained distance if only they might share deeply in the culture and life of men beyond the horizon and discover the problems and methods of their medicine. Such travelers have learned significantly because they have remembered that medicine is not only a scientific discipline and a knowledge of skills, but a social approach and an expression of human compassion as well. The aims of medicine, especially in its applied form, have been attained only "when vitally united with every source of light and experience in the human mind."

It was inevitable that the medicine of China and the medicine of the Western world should meet. China did not live for millenniums in isolation behind a Great Wall, as so many have thought. The Long Wall of Ten Thousand Li was, rather, a binding force that held the old empire together to resist intruders, while through its many gateways men traveled back and forth, exchanging the riches of East and West. The tribute of kings and the treasure of many nations passed through those archways, and no exchange was more significant than that of medical knowledge.

The caravan that journeyed to search for Iranian horses for Emperor Wu of the Han Dynasty included physicians among its personnel. They traveled across desert wastes and snowy mountain ranges from China to Iran, the journey lasting twelve years. The Chinese physicians came back from Iran

with drugs that proved, in the long run, to be more significant
for China than the horses that the emperor desired.

When Kubilai Khan invaded Europe, he took physicians
along who exchanged ideas with Iranian doctors. Both to
them and to the doctors they met in Turkey they taught the
method of inoculation against smallpox with powder from
the scabs.

But that was only the beginning of the interchange. The
Nestorian priests who reached China in the seventh century
took with them the balms and simples that were used in the
monasteries and hospices of Europe in those early centuries.
Other religious travelers followed, and the Nestorians came
to China again just before A.D. 1300. About that time the
Polos visited the Mongol rulers and acquainted them with
the trade and religion, the medicine and the political traditions of medieval Italy.

During the sixteenth century European culture began to
penetrate China, largely through the work of a few scholarly
missionaries, many of them Jesuits. The most eminent of
these missionaries was Matteo Ricci, who reached Peking in
1601. His scholarly discussions, together with those of later
Jesuits, covered the fields of ethics, mathematics, and astron-
omy. In 1692, three Jesuit priests were able to treat and cure
the eminent Emperor K'ang Hsi, when ill with malaria, with
the cinchona bark of Peru which the Vatican had but lately
forwarded to them.

And who knows what medicaments the ships' physicians
brought to China in the caravels of Portugal and in the trading ships of Holland and Britain during the sixteenth and
seventeenth centuries?

The Chinese themselves were no mean travelers. Before
the Portuguese traveler, Rafael Perestrello, reached the China

coast in 1516, "Chinese map makers showed a considerable acquaintance with Asia, from Japan to the Red Sea and from the Siberian border to Malacca, a region, as Father Henri Bernard has recently pointed out, greater in extent than was known to contemporary European cartographers."

From their travels they brought back opium—the Arabs called it *afyun*—as well as spices, cloves, and pepper, and the like, to enrich both their culinary and their medical art.

Religious devotees, too—Fa Hsien, Hsüan Tsang, and many others—crossed the almost impassable Himalayas to study Buddhism at its source in India. Returning, they brought with them rules for diet and the principles of nutrition that became a part of the Chinese tradition. They worked miracles, too, in preventing the spread of epidemics.

Gradually, far too gradually, appreciation began to dawn in men's minds of cultures overland or across the seas. The travels of pilgrims and envoys, traders and missionaries made that appreciation possible.

Thus it came about, after the fifteenth century, that West and East were driven irresistibly outward, whether by commercial impulse, by religion or philosophy, or by art or medicine. When they met, understanding grew.

Many of the early travelers were merely curious, eager to record the unusual rather than to learn the inner thought of others who practised medicine. Too many, whether from China or from the West, started with unconcern, almost contempt, each for the other. Too often they went out with a sense of superiority, asserting, as in the case of China, that theirs was the Middle Kingdom; while men of the West assumed that light was a commodity heaven bestowed in special measure upon their nations. Centuries passed before those who journeyed really conceded that others, too, had wisdom.

The truly fearless ones were bound to meet, for their spirits were kin, their courage and tenacity similar. The observations of Li Shih-chen and of Schmiedeberg were of similar substance. So, too, were Hippocrates and Pien Ch'iao kindred spirits, though they lived half a world apart. Osler and Chang Chung-ching, masters of internal medicine, were teachers who left an ineffaceable impression on all whom they taught.

It was natural that, at the outset, doctors from the West, trained in the methods of laboratory science, should approach Chinese medicine with skepticism. What evidence of scientific inquiry was there down through its millenniums, without dissection, without controlled experiments? The scientists asked whether the remedies sold in the druggists' shops had anything but the weight of ancient use to commend them. What possible therapeutic value had dragon's teeth and tiger's bones and deer's marrow?

Yet within the lifetime of doctors from the West who came and lived understandingly and sympathetically in China, there came about a gradual change in this attitude. In some of the ancient medical lore, there appeared unsuspected values. The old approaches to diagnosis and treatment were not utterly without reason. Cures were achieved that the Western doctor could not easily explain. He began to ask himself how it was that time had brought such a mature understanding of human nature to the trained Chinese physician, and what had made him so quick to realize the social and religious and economic factors behind the external manifestations of disease.

To have lived in China at a time when Westerners were beginning to try to understand Chinese medical thought, and when China was beginning to recognize the need of the Western approach to scientific medicine, has been a unique experience.

This book is the personal record of how one American doctor discovered that medicine was a builder of bridges between nations and cultures.

I

WHAT JOURNEYINGS!

前人開路
後人行

An earlier generation blazes the trail
On which a later generation travels.

"COME to China as soon as you can. You are needed here far more than in India!"

This summons from Dr. Harlan Beach, who was in China making a survey for the Yale University Mission, was startling to one who thought of himself as anchored in India.

"Nothing you can ever accomplish in Bombay can equal the opportunity that awaits you in Changsha," Dr. Beach's letter continued. "I have just been up the Yangtze River to visit Hunan. That province has hitherto been thought antiforeign, but a new treaty has been signed making it possible for Westerners to reside and work there. The people are intelligent, well educated, full of initiative. They are sure to welcome a trained

Western doctor who comes to start a modern hospital. Before long you will be able to launch a university medical school. This is where you ought to work. Come without delay!"

Those were alluring words: "You will be able to launch a university medical school." It was the goal I had always set before myself, but it was in India that I had dreamed of realizing that goal.

Why leave India? My father and grandfather had worked here for years. I was the only American physician practising in Bombay. I had been born in Ahmednagar and brought up in Bombay within sight of the trains that passed our back yard on the way to Calcutta and Madras, to Agra and Delhi, and the valleys of the Ganges and the Indus. I had made my first coppers for sweetmeats by standing at our gate in the dawn and selling tracts to workers on their way to the cotton mills. It was those sweetmeats, tasty but contaminated, that gave me typhoid fever, and it was during my convalescence that I decided to be a doctor. India was home and I had always intended to work there.

Soon after getting my medical degree at Johns Hopkins I was sent to India by the United States Public Health Service and was reporting regularly on the epidemic of bubonic plague, then at its height. One of my duties was to inspect freight steamers clearing for American ports, to make sure that adequate rat guards had been used and that every piece of freight had been disinfected according to regulations. In addition, I was being trained in plague laboratory methods by the distinguished Russian scientist, Haffkine, who had devised the antiplague vaccine that was saving countless lives in India and overseas. Why go from a certain opportunity in India to an unknown situation in China at this time of crisis? Why take our infant son, Ted, into the China Sea, where the war between Russia and Japan was at its peak?

I had heard about the plan for a Yale University Mission in China the year before I came out to India. I knew about the famous meeting that had taken place the year before at the home of Anson Stokes in New Haven, when the plan was laid before a group of friends. They were told that the prototypes being followed in the Yale plan were the Oxford and the Cambridge University missions in India. The invitation to China had first come to me then. I had been asked to go out with Thurston, their pioneer appointee in 1902, to be their first physician in China. My India background had led me then to decline. Why should the issue be raised now?

I turned again to Dr. Beach's letter: "to launch a university medical school." This chance had not come to me in India, for there were government medical colleges already established in the capital cities of the chief provinces. It was evident, moreover, that American societies were not prepared, at that time, to share in establishing a university medical college under Christian auspices in India. The vision of doing my life work in India began to fade. In China, perhaps, lay the greater opportunity. After weeks of wavering I decided to go.

As we steamed across the Indian Ocean I kept thinking of my father, Edward Sackett Hume, who had brought his young bride to Bombay and had spent nearly thirty years there at the head of a high school for Indian boys and girls. He had taught me to love Latin and Greek so that all through life the classics were my natural companions. It was his influence that made me seek out Oriental children as the friends of my boyhood.

I thought back, too, to my mother, born in Madura, and to her father, John Eddy Chandler, who had crossed the Indian Ocean sixty years earlier, to spend the rest of his life as a missionary in South India.

I recalled vividly the stories Grandmother had told me of her voyage to India with Grandfather Robert Wilson Hume in 1839. They had sailed to Bombay on the stout brig *Waverly* out of Salem. I could almost see the *Waverly* battling the monsoon weather on this same ocean. Grandmother Hume had told me that, although she was glad to share her husband's missionary experience, it had been hard to have him insist on exchanging Bibles, rather than rings, at their wedding. A ring would be too worldly for a missionary's wife, he said, as would the precious brooch he asked her to leave behind, although a brooch was then an essential part of every gentlewoman's attire. It had been hard enough to leave home and friends.

Most fascinating of all had been Grandmother's story of her meeting with the Sultan of Zanzibar. When the *Waverly* put in at Zanzibar for water and supplies, the sultan, delighted to welcome strangers, invited the captain and his passengers to a reception at the palace. As the guests were seated in the great reception hall, the sultan pointed to something in one corner of the room and asked the travelers if any of them knew what it might be. Queen Victoria had sent it to him as a gift. It was an old-fashioned square piano lying on its back with its legs pointing up as if it were some huge insect.

When Grandmother told the sultan what it was, he ordered the servants to right the instrument. Grandmother was an accomplished musician and was still mournful at having had to leave her piano behind. She played for the sultan all the gay tunes she could remember. He kept calling for another tune and still another. Presently he sent his chief steward on an errand. In a few minutes the wide central doors flew open and the steward returned, bringing with him six young, black, Zanzibar girls. The sultan led them to Grandfather Hume and said, "Sir, please take these six young women with you and leave *her* with me," pointing to Grandmother.

That was Grandmother's first adventure in the Orient. Now

I, too, was going to an unknown land, and I wondered what lay ahead of us, in 1905, as we made our way into the Pacific.

I was soon to find out. It was a relief, too, as we made the four-day run up the China coast from Hong Kong to Shanghai, to learn that we were not to be involved in war. One noon the captain posted on the bulletin board a message saying that Russia and Japan had just signed an armistice. Japan was victorious. For the present there would be no more fighting in the China Sea.

On the afternoon of June 19 the water round the ship became definitely muddy. The chief officer, passing us on deck, stopped to say that we had been in the estuary of the Yangtze River since early morning. By straining our eyes we could make out the shore line that resembled the margins of a coral reef in the Pacific, barely rising above the level of the waves.

Presently the ship made a sharp left turn and we found ourselves in the Whangpoo River which was crowded with boats of every description, from sampans to ocean steamers. More striking than anything on the shore were the junks we met, each with a huge eye painted on either side of the bow. As he saw us watching them, fascinated, the chief officer told us that junks up and down the China coast were all decorated with these eyes. Without them, people thought, a boat could not see where it was going. We, too, as we went up and down China's rivers through the years, discovered what reassurance those watchful eyes brought to both mariners and passengers.

As we rounded a bend in the river, a large junk, carrying full sail, darted across our bow. There was a clanging of bells as the enraged pilot ordered the helm turned sharply. The chief officer saw our alarm and told us that the junk captains did this constantly and that they thought that, if they could get across directly in front of a large steamer, it would cut them off from the influence of any evil spirit that might be pursuing them. He breathed easier himself as he saw that the pilot had managed to avoid hitting the offender. "As you go up the Yangtze River," he commented, "you will find that many of the river pilots keep baskets filled with stones on the bridge. They hurl them at junkmen who try a trick like that. It is far more effective than profanity!"

A little after five o'clock we tied up at the Shanghai dock, went ashore, and rode off in rickshas to spend our first night in China. Within the very first hour ashore I was reminded that I was not a traveler merely, or a sight-seer off some round-the-world ship. We had scarcely got settled in our room at the little hotel when the amah whom we had brought along from Hong Kong to help take care of our little son, Ted, came to me and said, "Master, Number One Room boy makee sick. He ask you please see his sickness." She was an itinerant amah and could speak only pidgin English. I didn't realize just then that she was using a universal phrase when she said "see his sickness." It was the age-old phrase with which all Chinese asked for a doctor's aid.

On the third night after reaching Shanghai we were on our way again. The comfortable river steamer started quite early in the morning and, by the time we were well awake, we looked out of our stateroom windows to find ourselves steaming along close to the shore of the River. The fields seemed to stretch from the ship's side into the distance as far as the eye could see. They were a lovely light green, the green of young rice. In some patches the rice shoots were still being transplanted from seedbeds to the water-logged patches that would soon become real paddy fields. Splashing along in one watery enclosure, we saw a big, lazy-looking water buffalo with a small boy riding along contentedly on his back. Only yesterday, we knew, that powerful animal had been pulling a heavy plow through the muddy field. Today he and his boy rider were taking life a little easier.

The River was full of junks. Shining in the morning sunlight, their hulls newly rubbed down with tung oil; sails brown, sails white, sails blue; sails square, sails triangular! Often there was just a framework of bamboo with a few ragged remnants of cloth left pressing against the mast, barely enough to catch a breath of wind. All the junks, big or little, seemed to be of different patterns. The captain translated for us what the Chinese pilot told him. "Every village, every town on the River," he said, "has its own type of junk. That squarish, freight-carrying junk over there hails from Nantung, a little place we shall pass presently. And that long boat beyond it is used on the Grand Canal running north from Hangchow to enter the River at Chinkiang. The sail patterns, like the junks, differ from place to place." Then he added, "I've been a pilot on this river for twenty years and I'm only beginning to distinguish them now. That big junk over there, struggling slowly against the current, the one with the tall mast, is a salt junk, headed for Hunan. It gets its cargo of salt down at the seacoast and carries it up to Changsha."

Changsha! We caught the name and listened eagerly, hoping to hear it again as the pilot told the captain about the boats on the River. It was the only word we could understand, but now, since he was talking about *our* destination, his whole conversation seemed to have meaning.

The captain translated what the pilot said about the inland city. Not many downriver people knew about Changsha—a few, perhaps, who had heard how it had withstood the attack of the Taiping Rebels—but scarcely any knew of it as a great trade center where the salt cargoes from the coast were shifted into much smaller boats.

Pointing to a string of cargo junks, the captain said they

should be of interest to a medical man. They had come down from Wanhsien at the head of the Yangtze gorges and carried cargoes of foxglove and monkshood and other medicinal herbs to be shipped overseas and used for medicines. The province of Szechwan, he told me, supplied 75 per cent of all the vegetable remedies used within China, as well as large amounts for shipment abroad. And all of it was carried down the Yangtze in cargo boats.

Three days aboard, and the River was still a mile wide. It was deep enough, too, for ocean steamers from Europe and America. As we steamed along, day after day, the River seemed to possess our being. Near the surface were shifting sandbars and dangerous currents; deeper down lay many hidden rocks. In its great flow and far depths there were the timelessness and steady strength of the life and tradition of old China. With its sources in a distant somewhere and its flood volume constantly increased by smaller streams and rivers, each tributary becoming part of the larger current, blending imperceptibly into its onflowing without stir or foam, the Yangtze was a symbol of the millenniums of Chinese history.

II

THE BLOCKED ARCHWAY

When you enter a neighborhood, ask what is forbidden;
When you enter a country, ask about the customs.

WE HAD finally turned into Hunan province and were entering
the Hsiang River that would carry us to Changsha, only a
hundred miles farther upstream. It was exciting to be so near
the end of the long journey that had brought us from Bombay.

Hunan looked lovely on that summer afternoon. The low
hills of red clay on our left were topped with many shades of
green, ranging all the way from the pale green of the young
bamboos to the dark, deep green of the camphor trees in the
dense groves. Ahead, we could see the river broadening out
into Tungting Lake. Two wooded islands lay off to our right.
The nearer of them, *Pien Shan*, Flat Island, looked like a raised
rocky bank. It was about a mile long and seemed quite unin-

habited except for pheasants and other birds. The more distant island, *Chun Shan*, the Island of the Prince, was covered with dark foliage, and we could make out clusters of huts along the shore. This was one of the fabled islands of China's history, where the Emperor Shun's consorts had pitched their tents, so the legend went, while their lord made a journey of inspection to the south.

I had become so absorbed in the scenery that I scarcely heard the footsteps that were coming near me, and the sound of a deck chair being drawn close up. In faultless English, a Chinese fellow passenger, evidently a man of the world, broke into my reverie. "Is this your first trip into Hunan?"

When he found out that I had never been here before, he told me that Hunan was his native province but that he had been away on business in Shanghai for so long that he felt like something of a stranger himself.

Here was someone, I thought, who knew the country and could tell me much that I wanted to know, so I pressed him to talk to me. He hadn't been in Hunan for over five years and was curious to see how his fellow provincials had reacted to the recent developments in politics, especially to the treaty which, a couple of years earlier, had made Hunan province accessible for travel by foreigners. The treaty, he said, provided that foreigners might live at Changsha, the capital. Some of the old-timers, the conservative gentry there, were still protesting, saying that the phrase "at Changsha" did not give foreigners the right to reside *within* the city. The year before, a Britisher had tried twice to go inside and rent a house within the city walls, but each time he had been removed by squads of soldiers at the governor's order. It might well be that the local Hunan gentry, who had been putting great pressure on the governor to keep foreigners away, would now get into serious conflict with the Peking Government.

The Chinese gentleman stopped to remark that we were now actually at the edge of the lake. "This region, where Tungting Lake pours its waters into the Yangtze River," he told me, "is spoken of everywhere as the rice bowl of China. Each year two, sometimes three, rice crops are harvested here. They ship the rice out in huge junks, much of it down to sea-coast provinces."

I was far more interested in what my friend was saying than in the river and its wooded shores. "Do you mean that the people of Hunan province," I challenged him, "are so conservative as to be still antiforeign? Don't they want any 'foreigners' living inside the capital? Why, I have just been sent out by a group of American university men to live *in* Changsha, to launch a modern hospital there. My colleagues and I hope to succeed in establishing an academy, and, eventually, a college of arts and a college of medicine. I am sure our trustees in America believe that the men they are sending out will be welcomed in Changsha."

The gentleman lighted a cigarette before replying. If he seemed perplexed, it was only for a moment. "How much do you know," he asked me, "about Boxer Year and recent Chinese politics?" Discovering how inadequately I was informed, he gave me some of the background for this hostility to foreigners.

The ten years prior to 1900 had been a bad period for China. One European power after another started to help itself, if not to actual territory, at least to a sphere of influence. In 1898 Germany anchored itself in the east of Shantung province, on that peninsula jutting out into the Yellow Sea, seized the main seaport, built a railroad from the coast to the provincial capital, and claimed the right to mining and other concessions through-out the province. Foreigners had but to make a strong protest about something, and the Manchu Court gave in without re-sistance. Immediately, patriotic secret societies had sprung up in rapid succession, concerned chiefly with driving out the Manchu Dynasty for the thoroughly inefficient way in which it was running the government.

Loyal Chinese, who believed themselves descendants of the Han and Ming dynasties, still regarded the Manchus as foreigners who since 1644 had usurped the throne and must not be allowed now to sell out China to Westerners. The strongest of the secret societies in the north was called Righteous Harmony Boxers. They determined to capture Peking and throw out the Empress Dowager, but the wily old ruler got wind of the plan and, with her usual astuteness, managed to turn their attack away from the Manchus and against the Westerners. She persuaded her political coterie that it was Americans and British, together with Germans and other Europeans, who were really to blame for the disorders in China.

Finally, the Boxers launched an attack against the foreigners in the walled capital at Peking, driving them back inside the British legation, which was defended against these assaults for many weeks. In midsummer, a relief expedition, consisting of troops from America and Britain and other European countries, as well as from Japan, marched up from Tientsin, dispersed the attacking Boxers, relieved the foreigners imprisoned in the legation, and threatened to capture the Empress Dowager. She, however, had made her escape to Sian, capital of Shensi province, and maintained her court there for several months. After that, she was permitted to return to her own palace in the capital, where she carried on in state as of old.

I asked whether her restoration was what had made the Hunanese so antiforeign.

"No," he replied, "but when the Allied Relief Expedition went up to Peking in the summer of 1900, the foreign forces fought Chinese troops every step of the way up from the sea and killed thousands of them."

Hunan was indignant about its proportion of the total annual indemnity that the Western powers had imposed. In addition, after the Hunanese had boasted that their province could defy Peking by not admitting foreigners, the Manchus had signed this treaty, permitting them to enter, reside, and trade at certain designated centers in the province. The provincials were angry. They were likely to continue indignant and resentful for a long time.

For nearly four hundred years, my acquaintance pointed out, foreign traders had invariably insisted that trade be carried on as they wished it, forgetting that the Chinese had every right to impose such restrictions as they chose. China was a nation of traders, and merchants had always been one of the four recognized social classes—scholars, farmers, artisans, traders. For centuries they sailed the four seas, down to the Pacific islands, westward to the Red Sea and the Persian Gulf. But it had been their aim merely to buy and sell, not to impose Chinese traditional ways.

The gentleman from Hunan concluded, "Look down our coastal line and see what has happened there these past four centuries, ever since the Portuguese made their first landing. At each point it has been a story of opening fire, of massacre, of seizure, and, if any foreigner was killed in a fray, of insisting on an indemnity, either a cash payment or the cession of a piece of territory, frequently both. Right here in this province, two British missionaries lost their lives three years ago at the hands of an angry mob. It was only a hundred miles or so to the west of this place. The usual thing happened. The British consul was sent up on a gunboat, and, before long, the Peking Government agreed that an indemnity should be paid and that foreigners should have their rights of residence in Hunan province extended."

Then, as something on the shore caught his eye, he said, "Look over there at that stone arch through which the main highway passes, right there on the shore near us. I heard about it down in Shanghai, but I never saw it till now. You see that the gateway, standing at the very entrance of the province, is completely blocked up with stones and bricks and lime. I suppose all traffic has to detour through the village. The gentry of Hunan have blocked it as a sign that they don't want outsiders to come into the province."

The words of my fellow passenger gave me a sudden jolt. What about the trustees in New Haven who were so sure that Changsha would receive me and my colleagues with open arms? What about the clinical work that I had planned, the campaigns of vaccination against smallpox and typhoid, the medical school? There was nothing to do but to go and see for myself. I couldn't turn back here.

Darkness was falling rapidly as the ship stopped for the night, quite close to the shore. A pair of pheasants, startled by the rattle of the anchor chain, flew up with a whir from the brush beyond the blocked archway.

III

THE CITY OF
THE LONG SANDS

攻　攻
心　城
為　為
上　下

Capturing the city is secondary;
Capturing the heart is primary.

THE hubbub and excitement were unbelievable as our ship warped up to the pier at Changsha, where a motley crowd was waiting. Even before the engines stopped, hundreds of men stood on the very edge of the dock, trying to leap on board.

What a river front it was! What forbidding city walls! We had been hearing about Changsha for a year, but

A hundred hearings do not equal one seeing.

As the crowd pressed down to board the ship, I kept asking myself: friendly or hostile? I soon saw that most of the men were just coolies looking for the chance to take baggage ashore. Some of them were runners from the countless inns on River Street. At least fifty swarmed onto the passenger decks before the ship was made fast. Presently, in the middle of that seething crowd, a familiar face appeared. Warren Seabury, my academic colleague who had reached Changsha a year before me, had come to welcome us. After assembling the baggage, he packed us away in sedan chairs and told the bearers where to take us. I looked at the jammed street ahead and wondered whether we would get through.

We had just started toward the city wall when, suddenly, we saw a huge crowd gathered round a poster on the wall of the police station near the city gate. I made the chair bearers slow up until Seabury could arrive and tell me what the poster was about. It looked threatening. He came up and read it carefully.

"Evidently the Hunan gentry," he said, "have made pressure on Governor Ts'ên to issue an edict announcing that the government will not stamp the deeds of any property sold to foreigners inside the city walls of Changsha. Such a sale is absolutely forbidden. We may have trouble getting a place for our preparatory school and hospital."

A moment later we came up to the Little West Gate. It was a tunnel-like opening that confronted us, cut right through the massive city wall. Was this to be another blocked archway? What we saw, looming up in front of us, was an opening like an entrance to an ancient medieval dungeon. When my wife first looked up at it, she groaned and said, "Are we going to live *inside* that wall? I shall never be able to sleep at night. I shall feel as if a great stone mass were crushing me."

After we had passed through the tunnel and come out onto the city street, the noise and clatter became incredible. Were they just people going about their daily occupation, or was a riot brewing? Yet with all our concern, we felt at once an irresistible fascination about those streets. The life of the city seemed to pulse back and forth, back and forth, through each of those arteries. We passed many little open-front shops that had no need for window dressing. Coolies staggered by with loads of rice or vegetables, or even with great beams or blocks of stone for some building.

Sometimes the burden we saw them carrying was more precious than wood or stone. From above the rim of the woven bamboo basket at the end of a carrying pole, a little child in a gay coat peered at us, wondering. The bearer shouted to the crowd for gangway as he swung along. "Lean a little! Give me room!" We watched many a coolie stop at a tiny teashop for a sip of hot tea, while others lingered for a penny whiff from the public tobacco pipe carried everywhere by venders who would turn the long, jointed, bamboo stem toward the prospective smoker.

Mothers pushed their little children behind them as they saw us coming, to hide them from the "evil eye." Some held their noses as we passed. The amah told us once that the smell of the Westerner was so characteristic that Chinese recognized our presence without even seeing us. Some of the youngsters, my American colleague told us later, followed the sedan chairs shouting "foreign devil." It was fortunate, that first afternoon, that we didn't know what passers-by were saying.

On one street we met an old grandmother, dressed in a padded blue coat and trousers, perched on a wheelbarrow. She seemed to be reveling in the sights and sounds of the busy city street. Ordinarily her tiny bound feet limited the range of her travel to the family courtyard in the country village, but today she was in the provincial capital! Precariously seated on one side of the barrow, she was balanced on the other side by her day's purchases, tied in a bright square of cloth, that included gay boxes of sweetmeats and a couple of Yünnan hams. Nor had she forgotten her little white teapot and her water pipe. I wondered whether she would ever become my patient.

Soon we reached South Gate Main Street and turned into the entrance that later we always described as "next door to Yung Lung Cash Shop." The houses were not numbered and one always indicated a residence by its proximity to a well-known shop or school. Just before we reached the entrance, Seabury caught up with us. "Don't be alarmed," he called out, "about those men in uniform across the street. The governor is personally responsible for the safety of all Westerners in the city. By his special direction, two armed guards are on duty in that little sentry house, day and night. They will keep track of all your movements and will report about all your visitors to the chief of police. They are instructed to escort you whenever you leave the house."

Once inside the front entrance we went straight ahead for a few yards, then swung left, left once more, then right, and through the massive gate of the main doorway into the front courtyard. We were to learn that most Chinese houses were approached by this sort of winding way, a relic of an old belief that evil spirits might be seeking entrance and that they could be thrown off the scent by right-angled turns in the road. Sometimes a big dragon screen, ten feet high, placed in front of the main gate, would serve the same purpose.

From the front courtyard we were carried still farther in, through a corridor, across still another courtyard, till, at our own front door, the bearers set down the sedan chairs. We all started to explore this Chinese house which was to be our residence for the time being. The house was built within high walls on each side. We learned that these were fire walls, and that everywhere in the crowded city it was only these walls that afforded fire protection. We were glad enough to be so far back from the main street. We were in an enclosed cubicle of a house, shut away from outer noises, protected from fires. So far, so good. But I was not to find out for a long time whether Changsha—the City of the Long Sands—was as threatening a place as it seemed that first day.

IV
WEST ARCHWAY STREET

百聞不如一見

A hundred hearings do not equal one seeing.

BEFORE I began work in Changsha it was thought best that I devote a year to learning the Chinese language, so I removed with my family and my teacher, Yang, to Kuling, a mountain settlement about three hundred miles away. For me as for others Kuling was truly a "magic mountain."

During that first winter Teacher Yang gave me a good start on my Chinese vocabulary and also told me that I should have a Chinese surname; no Chinese, he said, could possibly pronounce my Western name. So we hunted through the standard list in *The Hundred Family Surnames*, a list that was not less than a thousand years old. Through the centuries the list

had grown, until it was now far more important than any social register in the Western world. Among the surnames one
was found for me, and I soon learned, when anyone asked me,
"*Hsien shêng, kwei hsing?*—Before-born, what is your honorable name?"—to reply without hesitation, "*Pi hsing Hu*—My
unworthy name is Hu." Now I was Dr. Hu (pronounced Hoo)
and could be identified anywhere in China. Life had begun
at twenty-nine.

When we returned to Changsha in 1906 we settled again
in the temporary residence on South Gate Main Street and I
attacked my first problem—to find a place for the hospital.
After this year's interval I wondered if the hostility of the
Changsha gentry toward foreigners had subsided at all. Would
anyone be found willing to disregard the tradition of "Hunan
for the Hunanese"?

One evening, long after dark, the gateman announced a
caller. I received him in our formal guest hall, tea was served,
and we talked at first about inconsequential matters. I was glad
to discover how easy it had become to talk to a Changsha gentleman who didn't know a single word of English. Seabury
joined us while we were still chatting. Presently, after we all
sipped tea together, it looked as if our guest were leaving.
Just as we reached the door of the guest hall, he hesitated a moment, then said, "Could we sit down together for a few minutes longer? I have a little matter to report to you."

We listened eagerly as our guest told us about himself. He
was a master mason, he said, and took building contracts in
many parts of the city. He had heard in the Lutheran church
of which he was a member that we were looking for some property.

The contractor stopped and looked around carefully to make
sure that no one was listening. Then he added that he had
found a place for us—two desirable locations on *Hsi P'ai Lou,*

West Archway Street, a commercial thoroughfare leading from east to west through the center of the city.

"Don't let anyone hear you mention this," he warned. "The servants mustn't know anything about it. I will arrange for you to investigate." He bowed and went out.

On the following day Seabury and I walked down to investigate. The contractor had told us we must not think of going inside the property, because to do so would be dangerous to our entire program. The business houses along the street would become apprehensive if they thought a Western institution was to move in near them. "You just walk along outside and see how large the place is," he had instructed us. "Then you can see the plan I have drawn for you. I have been doing all the mason's work inside. It is a huge rice storehouse, with residences at the rear, and should be excellent for your school."

We walked slowly up and down the street, passing and repassing the huge, high-walled building. Little shops adjoined it right and left, but this place was large enough for the academy. It was tantalizing not to be free to go inside. Fifty-three paces along the street! We learned about the interior from the good drawings the contractor had made on a sheet of coarse yellow paper. Every room was shown, every courtyard marked. It was fully three hundred feet from the front gate to the back wall, yet all the doors, all the windows and terraces, even the back stairways to the roof were clearly shown on the diagram.

My chief interest was to find a place for a dispensary. In the same week that we were bargaining for the property for the academy, a Mr. Lo appeared, also after dark. We drank tea together and talked about the height of the river and the rice crops. Then he spoke out. Was it true that we wanted to rent property for our hospital? He would like to have us see the Central Inn. There were outhouses at the back where pigs were fed and fattened till they were ready for the butcher. All these, he felt sure, could be removed easily. The place would be ideal, he thought, right there in the center of the city, just across the street from where, he heard, a property had been offered us for a school. On his second visit, we agreed to rent his place. Then there was bargaining, and more bargaining. We wrote down everything in the first draft of the agreement: who would be responsible for repairs to the roof, who would get the deed of rental stamped in the registry office, whether the monthly rental payments were to be in "bright" dollars or in "commercial" dollars.

We got a great deal of insight into the current trading methods in Changsha. At the very last moment there was a hitch. We asked Mr. Lo to let us have the first rough copy of the agreement to keep in our records. Mr. Liu, our secretary, would write out fair copies for both owner and tenant. But the paper had disappeared. We hunted on the tea table where all the discussions had taken place. No one had left the group. Then, suddenly, sitting opposite Mr. Lo, I saw an end of the paper far up inside his long silk sleeve.

"Oh, yes, here it is," he said, seeing that I had observed it. "Do you want to keep it?" he inquired, not at all embarrassed. After that, nearly everything went smoothly. Mr. Liu acted as our middleman and purchased the property for the academy in his own name, thus avoiding collision with the city fathers. He also went through the form of renting the dispensary and hospital property for us. Privately, he signed separate agreements with us, binding himself to hold everything entirely for our use.

It took us several weeks before that old inn could really be put into shape for use as a hospital. There was a well near the front and one in a rear courtyard, giving us all the water we needed for washing and scrubbing. Insect powder was used in abundance throughout all the rooms, and all the walls were whitewashed repeatedly. New roof gutters were put up to carry off the downpours of rain that fell from February to June; new doors and windows were installed, with glass panes to replace the paper that had always been used. New skylights were put into many corners which had been almost totally dark.

Here, we agreed, will be the waiting and reception room, here the pharmacy and consulting room, there a small laboratory. Shall we have an operating room at the start or leave that till later?

No major surgical operation had hitherto been attempted in Hunan province, and our Chinese friends advised us to go slowly—very slowly—about undertaking major surgery. "Let your surgical work," they cautioned us, "be of the simplest sort. Do only what you are willing to attempt in the presence of a roomful of dispensary onlookers. Take no risks. Wait till people know you better. After a year or two, perhaps. Not sooner!"

So we postponed the operating room. There was a little whitewashed office for the doctor, and a bit of a corner where the orderly, T'ou Sz-fu, might sleep. Little else was needed. In fact, we should have made a very unfortunate impression on all our neighbors of the street guild if there had been any display, any extravagance. We merely fitted up four working rooms, two and two on each side of the corridor that opened out on the street. Here we should be right in among the people, with shopkeepers and innkeepers for neighbors. We determined to keep open house, so that everyone might be free to come and look around at will.

Finally, by the middle of November, 1906, we were ready. In front of the hospital building we put up a sort of balustrade, eight feet high, to keep passers-by from being too inquisitive. And there was a big black lacquered sign, seven feet long by three and a half feet wide, with four gold-lacquered characters: *Yali I Yüan*—Yale Court of Medicine.

Across the street a similar lacquered sign was hung: *Yali Hsüeh T'ang*—Yale Hall of Learning. Here we started the preparatory school for boys, which was to be the forerunner of the Yale-in-China college of the future, just as the dispensary was to be the forerunner of a modern hospital and medical college. The academy opened with fifty-three pupils.

The hospital staff was even less pretentious than the building. A friend introduced to us a Mr. Chou, who was literate and well mannered and said to be an ideal man for the job of gatekeeper. He was to be on duty all the time, to register dispensary patients in the morning, to keep out possible troublemakers, and to inspect all bundles coming in and going out. The rest of the active staff consisted, at the beginning, of but two persons: T'ou Sz-fu and myself. T'ou Sz-fu was a coolie off the street. Only a week before he came to work for me he had been earning a living by carrying huge buckets of water into the city from the famous "Sand Spring" outside the South Gate. He was broad shouldered and muscular, tidy and respectful, but little else. Even the sweeping of a floor was a task practically beyond his powers. Could I trust him when we were getting ready for an operation?

But we worked together, the two of us, for months on end. We tried to see that everyone who came felt welcome, and to make sure that everyone who registered went away feeling that he had gotten his money's worth. Only thus could medicine build a bridge of friendship in the City of the Long Sands.

V

"FIFTY CASH! NO LESS!"

Bargaining is as necessary to trade as poling to a vessel.

It was opening day at the new hospital! The founders at Johns Hopkins couldn't possibly have been more elated, when they opened the great hospital in Baltimore in 1889, than I was, seventeen years later, when the unpretentious Yali I Yüan opened its doors at Changsha.

Here at last was a place in which I could put into practice something of what I had learned from my great teachers—Osler and Welch, Halsted and Kelly. I had now actually become the head of a hospital, even though a tiny one, located on a narrow, crowded street at the heart of a provincial capital, one of the storm centers of China.

We had inserted announcements for several days in the two leading newspapers of Changsha, and put up posters on the wall outside, saying that the dispensary would be open for patients on a certain morning. We had written formal letters to Governor Ts'ên and to the other provincial officials, saying that our "unpretentious building" was about to open and that we hoped, before long, to be honored by their official visits.

On that first morning, a crowd milled round the doorway, curious and hesitant, watching to see who would be the first to ask for treatment. Finally one man, looking a bit sheepish and as if he wanted to get it over with, stepped up to Gate-keeper Chou.

"How much is it?" he asked timidly. "I want to register!"

"Fifty cash apiece! No less!" Fifty cash was then equal to about two cents in United States currency. "You get a num- bered tally that entitles you to be seen by the doctor. First come, first served!"

"Make it forty cash," the patient shouted. "You should celebrate the opening day by offering reduced rates!"

I was seated inside but could overhear the candidate bar-gaining. I thought of the grain shops and the big cloth shops up the street. There was always a bid for business when a new place opened. And, of course, they seldom made a sale with-out a dialogue about the price. The common routine was for the shopkeeper to name his price, then for the customer to make a counterbid and to start moving away. The shopkeeper would wait till the prospective buyer had almost disappeared from sight, then shout for him to come back. Once agreement was reached, whether on the seller's terms or the buyer's, there was no deviation. It was like signing a legal deed. No wonder the first man up to register at our gate thought he, too, was entitled to a bargain.

But the gatekeeper remained adamant. "Fifty cash per per-son, no less! Think what you would have to pay if you went to consult some of the famous practitioners of our own Chinese medicine in Changsha. You would never get off so cheaply."

Then the second man, and the third; then a poorly dressed

woman carrying a child. She wanted to be examined herself and to have the doctor see her child as well. She wanted him to look at those swollen glands, and hoped it could all be done for one admission fee.

Then came a boy from the Yali School, who was not required to register. The school made a monthly grant to cover student medical care. Before long a dozen patients were seated quietly in the waiting room. Gatekeeper Chou struck a bell. No more registrations that morning!

While I sat there listening to the conversation at the registration desk, I thought back to the proclamation on the wall of the police station at the Little West Gate, the day we arrived. Would the local gentry, knowing that we were ready to start, try to move us away from the city? They had insisted, a few years earlier, on having an American engineer move his railroad tracks well to the east of the city so that they should not come too close to the southeast corner of the city wall or disturb the graveyards of their ancestors outside the South Gate. They knew all about us, of course, for Mr. Liu had taken the rental agreement to be stamped at the yamen. Transactions such as that could never remain secret in China.

I wondered, too, what the ordinary citizens were thinking of this new institution. Would they believe rumors about the "foreign doctor" and the medicines he was said to make out of the eyes of little children? Would they classify this new Westerner with the best of their own medical practitioners, or would they think of him as in the category with the diviner and the astrologer? These might, of course, be consulted by good citizens in medical emergencies, but they never ranked with the leading doctors.

As a matter of fact, during the previous week, some of the

well-known families had sent their servants over to ask about
our registration fees and the charges for treatment at the Yali
Hospital. There was no public dispensary in the city where the
poor could get treatment for a moderate fee.

We knew, of course, that not very many would come at first.
They would send scouts to watch, to test us, to report back to
their families. Then they would discuss us at home, and, if
not wholly dissatisfied, send others to look and inquire.

Mothers, of course, would be conservative. Every mother
in Changsha could treat her child with the right dose of rhu-
barb or licorice or cinnamon. She knew what the indications
were for these and all the other common drugs. She was certain to try them before coming to consult me. After all, I was
a "foreign doctor." How natural that she should hesitate about
me! If drugs failed, a mother could always go to a temple. She
had known from childhood that prayer at a temple often proved
effective. She had been taught that

> If there is prayer,
> There is bound to be an answer.

It was natural that in the atmosphere of a Chinese city where
religion and health were constantly thought of together, there
should be prayer and worship at the Yali Hospital as it began
its work. A Chinese pastor came over to lead the opening service. He read from the New Testament the story of the Healer
who, nearly two thousand years before, found a cripple lying
at the Pool of Bethesda and had startled him by asking, "Don't
you want to be made whole?"

It was a moving experience to follow the eyes of the group
that day as they listened to the speaker. "This hospital," he
told them, "is founded by followers of that same great Healer.
It is opening its doors in Changsha today, and hopes to min-

ister, as that Healer did, to all the people of this city. We invite
you to tell your friends about the Yali Hospital. Come with
them if they are inclined to be timid. They will soon learn that
this is a place of healing, where all may meet as friends."

☯

As the crowd thinned out on that first morning, a Hunan
countryman addressed me timidly: "From what province do
you come, sir? Are you perchance from Ningpo?"

Glancing at him, I saw that he had cataracts in both eyes.
He could probably see light and shadow, nothing more. Was
his inquiry a compliment, because he understood my Chinese,
or was he merely following the routine questioning?

"I can understand every word you say, sir," he added, "but
the people in the clinic this morning told me you were not a
native of Hunan, so I thought that you were, perhaps, from
Ningpo."

"No," I replied, "I am from America. I have not been in
Hunan very long and I speak Chinese very poorly!"

"You mustn't disparage yourself," he insisted. "Anyone
might mistake you for a native of Hunan. You speak clearly
and you know our little idioms so well. Did you say you had
been in Hunan but a short time?"

It gave me a tremendous lift to have the old man say this.
The time with Teacher Yang had evidently not been wasted.
He had taught me how to approach sick people acceptably.
Those first sentences that he drilled into me had been used
this very morning!

Ni ping liao chi t'ien?—How many days have you been ill?

Hsien shêng ti ping pu yao chin.—The gentleman's illness is
of no consequence.

K'uai hao la.—You will soon be well.

The old countryman went on questioning me. "Did you study the language right here in Changsha?"

"No, when I reached the city last year," I told him, "I didn't know a single Chinese sentence. Besides, we had no place for a hospital then. So I invited a Changsha teacher, Mr. Yang, to go with me up to a little village on the Lu Shan range in Kiangsi province. He taught me daily all through the winter. You have honored our hospital by coming to it on this opening day."

"And you, sir," the patient continued, "have learned the importance of our Chinese saying:

> If one's courtesy appears excessive,
> No one will find fault.

I listened to you as you addressed each patient in turn: 'What is your honorable name? What is your honorable place of abode?' and I knew you would make friends easily."

My guest left with a profound bow. "I shall come over before long to have you treat my eyes. I believe I can trust you to cut-with-the-knife."

It had been a memorable week. We were now really under way. The pigs had all been cleared out of the back courtyard of the Central Inn; the old building was washed and whitewashed, the space suitably subdivided for our simple needs. We had started, too, to organize the staff. We already had the doctor, the orderly, and the gateman. Obviously, since two of the men were to live on the premises, we needed a cook as well. Before employing anyone we held a sort of hospital town meeting, asking Mr. Liu, from across the street, to advise us. We agreed to his suggestion that, since we were using the old building that had once been the Central Inn, we employ one of the inn's former cooks. He bargained to serve three meals a day to the staff for three dollars per person per month, Chinese currency. This was the same rate that was to be paid for the boys' meals in the Yali Preparatory School. Only, as we had so small a staff, the meals would be simpler: three vegetables at each meal and occasionally a little meat.

VI
"HE KNOWS NO MEDICINE!"

三指活人性命
不為良相
便為良醫

He who revives man's life
With three fingers (on the pulse)
Is not a good statesman
But a good doctor.

AFTER two years we added a Chinese physician to the staff.
Dr. Hou had been trained as an apprentice in a Presbyterian
hospital in North China and his coming made a new link with
the people on West Archway Street. This Chinese medical
man treated them with the same methods that the "foreign
doctor" used, but he knew their language and their local customs so much better.

Soon after he arrived, we had a series of unusually full days in the dispensary, the crowds starting to pound on the front door soon after sunrise. The registration fee continued at fifty cash, and Gatekeeper Chou had barely enough bamboo tallies for the crowd.

At nine o'clock one morning Dr. Hou and I took our places at the clinic table, while T'ou Sz-fu, standing at the door of the crowded waiting room, wrestled with those who tried to squeeze past. His orders were to let in only three at a time to the doctors' consulting room.

Suddenly we heard shouts and the tread of many feet in the corridor; then loud commands: "*Hsiao hsin! Fang hsia!*— Carefully! Set the chair down!" Then, angrily: "Stand aside, you brats; this is a mandarin's official chair!" And, as they came to a halt: "So—slowly—on the ground! There we are! Please dismount, Great One!"

This was the first time an official had deigned to visit our humble quarters. The noise and clatter made one think a company of soldiers was marching in. Brushing the gateman aside, the bearers had insisted on carrying the sedan chair right into the inner court so that the occupant need not be exposed to the weather. They shouted their way in, as if they had brought the viceroy himself, then started to push humbler waiting dispensary patients out of the way. "This is a *taotai*; stand back!" they shouted to some inquisitive boys from the street who wondered why an official should come to see the foreign doctor.

My friends in America could not have understood how elated we felt because a *taotai* had come as a patient. They would have been duly impressed, however, if they could have seen the patient himself as he stepped out from behind the heavy blue curtains of the sedan chair. The rear bearer raised the two long poles, tipping the chair forward, and the gorgeously attired mandarin emerged. His official hat was topped with a light blue "button," shaped like a huge marble an inch in diameter. He was an official of the fourth rank. Below his splendid deep purple gown I could see the striped silken skirt of the official costume. Behind, a long queue appeared from beneath the mandarin hat, with a silken tassel a foot long braided in where actual hair ended.

Listening, I heard the insistent voice of the mandarin. "You don't know the difference," he said severely to T'ou Sz-fu, "between me and a coolie off the street! Don't you see the button on my mandarin cap? Don't you recognize that I am of *taotai* rank? You poor fool!"

"Yes, Great One, I know you are a *taotai;* but this foreign doctor would dismiss me in an instant if I admitted you out of turn. He has made strict rules, Great One, and enforces them. I am not worthy, Great One, to stand opposite you!"

Dr. Hou and I smiled at the dialogue outside, but agreed that the visit of this official might do much to establish the reputation of the hospital in the community. People would admit that we had "arrived."

When the door opened for the next batch of patients, the official forced himself through, muttering in a low voice to the servant who followed close at his heels. It didn't look as if he had come entirely of his own volition, for, as he took his seat on a bench at the side of the room, he related in a loud voice the rumors he had heard about the foreign doctor and the strange things he expected to experience.

Presently his number was called and he took his seat at my right, at one end of the table. Fortunately, Dr. Hou had drilled me in the various opening phrases that courtesy demanded in greeting a new patient, especially one of official rank.

"Please sit down, sir. What is your honorable name?"

"My name is Li. But I didn't know I should be able to understand you. I thought all foreigners spoke an unintelligible jargon."

"I speak very poorly, but I am trying to learn your language. Where is your honorable residence?"

"My humble cottage is in Liuyang. You know, it is a city famous for its clever physicians and its excellent drugstores."

"What is your honorable age?"

"I was born in the year *Kwei hai,* so I am forty-five."

"What are the symptoms of your honorable disease?"

Thus we struggled through the traditional liturgy of question and answer, until I got a clue as to the cause of his fever. I arranged a couple of books at my right, their edges square with the sides of the table. Then, lifting his left hand gently and pushing back the long silk sleeve, I placed his wrist on the books so that I could get at the pulse. It was fortunate that I had the left wrist by me, for, as I was to learn, anything else would have violated the rules. The patient seemed pleased at my attention to these details and observed, "You appear to know, foreign doctor, that it is really a great art to feel the pulse correctly. You have done well to place my wrist on a pile of books."

I took my time in feeling the pulse. Probably old Dr. Wang Shu-ho, who had lived seventeen hundred years earlier, would have criticized my technique. No one else in China had studied pulse signs in such detail since then. I wondered whether he would have interpreted this patient's pulse as I did.

Discovering that the patient was feverish, I reached for the thermometer, placed it in his mouth, and told him to keep his lips closed tightly. This proved to be an almost impossible ordeal. He was wondering, I realized, whether I had started to force some strange medicine into him. He was cornered, however, and, though almost exploding with excitement, could say not a word until I removed the thermometer. Then a storm of rage broke loose. He shouted at his attendant, cursing all his ancestors. "Why did you bring me here? Why didn't you watch me more carefully? Why did you let the foreigner put that strange hard thing inside my mouth? You can see that he knows no medicine!"

Then in a loud voice, so that all in the dispensary could hear, "Did you see? Did you take note that he felt only my left pulse? How in the world can a doctor make a diagnosis unless he feels both pulses, the right as well as the left? Even now, with all his examining, he knows only half the story!"

There was no use offering suggestions or writing a prescription. The *taotai* stalked deliberately out of the room, holding his head high, while the poor servant followed behind, abject, disgraced.

As the *taotai* moved slowly to the door, still grumbling about my lack of medical knowledge, it suddenly flashed into my mind that he had been used as a test case by fellow members of the gentry. They had heard, I presumed, of our mounting attendance at the dispensary. Perhaps they feared that we might be getting too strong a foothold in Changsha.

I remembered, too, that it was a full year since the student strike across the street at the Yali School. We could never forget that morning when the students over there refused to attend classes. Some of them said they couldn't understand the pronunciation of the Chinese teacher of physics who had come to us from Shantung province. Others said they didn't like the requirement of daily chapel attendance. And there were still other excuses. It was twenty years before we found out what had really happened. Some of the boys were sons of well-known Changsha families who had risked a good deal to patronize this "foreign school." The more conservative members of the gentry had gotten together and persuaded the leaders in our student body to strike. They wanted to see whether, in addition to being good teachers, we were disciplinarians as well. Two lines in the age-old *Trimetrical Classic* said it clearly:

> To nurture without disciplining
> Proves the father at fault!

When fathers found out that the Yali faculty stood firm, they called off the strike. They were really grateful that there was an institution close by where their sons would be rigidly disciplined.

That afternoon I had a consultation with Dr. Hou. Why had that patient called my procedure only half complete? Dr. Hou knew Chinese medical lore, of course, and explained things to me very patiently. From time immemorial, he said, the Chinese have been taught that there are three pulse points on each wrist. Each of these six points gives the doctor information about a particular organ. Thus the points on the left wrist —Chinese doctors always begin their examination of men on the left, while with women they start on the right—reveal the state of the heart, the liver, the kidney. The points on the right wrist reveal the condition of the lungs, the spleen, the genital organs.

So that was why the *taotai* was so indignant! I had felt of the three points on the left wrist, and stopped there, leaving him certain that I had no knowledge at all about the other three vital organs.

"All the people who looked on agreed with him that your diagnosis was only half complete," Dr. Hou concluded. "The *taotai* didn't care what you discovered with your thermometer, and neither will anyone else in Changsha. They have never heard of measuring the degrees of fever exactly, but they feel sure that the pulse is the secret to exact diagnosis and they all saw that you felt only one pulse."

I was discouraged. My first interview with an official patient had ended with his going off contemptuously. I began to wonder whether the reputation of the hospital had not suffered as a result of the morning's encounter. I ought to have provided special attention for our first mandarin. I should have known that this member of the official class, famous for his scholarship, would be listened to eagerly when he made his report to the gentry of Changsha. Now he was likely to tell them that, in his opinion, I knew no medicine.

VII
THE FIRST INPATIENTS

Better to save one man's life
Than to build a seven-story pagoda.

WITHIN two weeks after we opened the dispensary, a seriously sick boy was brought in, a student from the Yali School. I had hoped from the first that inpatient work would begin with a hard case. Then we should be able to show what scientific medicine could really do. And now, here he was, our first inpatient, thrust on us before we had a medical ward opened, before even a single ward bed was ready. But some of the beds from the old Central Inn were still stored in the back court, all washed and disinfected. We put one up at once at the back of the waiting room. There were no springs, of course, but there was a mattress of fiber rope, crisscrossed in a way all Hunanese understood. The boy's mother had brought along the *p'u-kai* and the *pei-wo*, bedding from his own bed at home, so we were sure we could make him comfortable.

The proctor brought him in personally. "He is one of our brightest students. Do all you can for him, Doctor Hume. Although the dispensary has been open for two weeks, and your morning attendances have been growing, this will be your first 'live-in-the-hospital patient.' If this student improves rapidly, it will mean a lot for the reputation of the Yali Hospital."

The patient was breathing rapidly, his face was flushed, and he had a high temperature. It didn't take long to examine his chest, to do a leukocyte count, to discover that he had lobar pneumonia. We got him into bed, a history chart was hung up, and modern inpatient practice got under way in the capital of Hunan province.

This was what I had been waiting for—a medical case that would really test my skill. All the hot summer days of hunting for the right building, all the drudgery of getting a lease written for the simple quarters we had rented, of getting the document stamped at the yamen, all this suddenly faded into insignificance. The opportunity had come. All that Osler had taught us about pneumonia rose up before me like a vivid, ineffaceable guide. It ought not to be hard to follow those principles.

And yet! Here lay a terribly ill patient; and I was without a trained nurse to watch, without even an experienced orderly to wait on him. There was no one but the coolie, T'ou Sz-fu, and this was a case of double lobar pneumonia.

So I let the boy's mother stay at the bedside to watch him constantly, feed him and give him medication under supervision. T'ou Sz-fu did all he could to help, but as the hours passed, he became distraught. I could hear him muttering, "What will happen if the lad really becomes seriously ill?"

All three of us, the mother, T'ou Sz-fu, and I, took turns watching the boy that first night. The following day he was no better. The mother was relieved when her sister came over to make inquiries. The family had sent her to find out whether the young relative was suffering any harm from being in the strange environment. She watched at the bedside with the boy's mother, and I could overhear the conversation.

"How can you trust a young foreign doctor so completely as to put the boy in his care?"

The mother nodded. She was beginning to be apprehensive, too.

"Perhaps it would have been wiser to have had him at home; to have sent for Doctor Mei from the North Gate and, if his prescription didn't work, for Doctor Lung from the Little West Gate. Their medicines would undoubtedly have gone right to the spot. I must watch this foreign doctor. I brought the boy because Younger Brother, also a student in the Yali School, told me not to be afraid."

"Ai-ya! Why did you listen to Younger Brother? We should never have allowed you to come here. Why don't you take him home?"

The boy grew steadily worse. On the morning of the third day, T'ou Sz-fu came and knelt before me, clasping his hands together like one in prayer.

"Please, sir, send the boy home."

"But why?"

"Oh, don't you see how ill he is? You are a famous foreign doctor and I am only a poor ignorant peasant, but I can see how dangerous his condition is. Please, sir, send him home."

"Yes, I know he is very ill. But it is just because his condition is so critical that I want to use all the most modern treatment. We must fight hard to save his life."

"Yes, sir, you are very wise. But I know what the people on our street are saying. I know their thoughts. You don't understand, sir. Suppose he should die in the hospital. All your work of these past weeks would be undone. Please get Teacher Liu to explain it all to you this afternoon when you have your Chinese lesson. He will tell you whether I am right or wrong. But please take no chances now. I beg you to send the boy home before there is an accident."

I felt deep resentment at being told by an untrained coolie what I ought to do for the critically ill patient and was irritated beyond words.

And yet! And yet, T'ou Sz-fu did know the psychology of his countrymen. I didn't. Perhaps he was right. I sat and reflected. After a while I sent for the mother and the aunt and told them very quietly that the boy would probably be more comfortable at home, but that I would send medicine with him.

I could see how immensely relieved they were. As the bearers carried the stretcher away down the narrow street, I mourned to think that I was letting our very first patient be taken home before we had made a fair fight for his life. All the months of preparation, the first weeks in the dispensary, more cases coming every day! Such a promising outlook for modern medicine! Some day, I had been hoping, the governor would send his wife to be treated, or, at the very least, one of his high-up yamen secretaries.

And now—a sense of frustration with the very first inpatient. Was the whole beginning to end in failure?

That afternoon, my Chinese lesson dragged. Repeating, intoning those tedious sentences that Teacher Liu was drilling into me seemed a bore. I was thinking of the boy with pneumonia back there in his poor home, without nursing, without stimulants, without appropriate nourishment. Would I ever forgive myself for letting him go? I turned from the lesson sheets. "Teacher Liu, why did T'ou Sz-fu beg me to send that sick young Li home?"

I told him about the incidents of the day, and how T'ou Sz-fu had called my attention, during the morning, to his desperate condition, urging me not to keep him in the hospital another hour.

"What did you do?" he asked.

"Against my better professional judgment, I yielded to T'ou Sz-fu's plea. I'm sorry to admit that I let the mother take the boy home."

"T'ou Sz-fu was entirely right. You would have made a serious blunder if you had let him stay. If he had died in the ward, so early in the life of our new hospital, the whole population of the city might have turned against you. They might have raided the Yali Hospital and destroyed it. Worse still, word about the death would have spread along every road that leads out from the capital. Before long all the corners of the province would have known. You might have set back the progress of Western medicine for years in this conservative province."

"But what would cause such an uproar?"

"Doctor Hume, you don't understand." Teacher Liu explained that at death the body is kept in the home awaiting the return of the soul. It is very serious for death to occur away from home, for the wandering soul may not find the body. The soul is allowed, however, to rejoin the body in a "pavilion of waiting," easy of access to the returning soul. He said I must do nothing to give the people offence during these early years.

"But how long will I have to be so cautious?"

"At least two years," he replied. "During that time, if things go well, people will begin to trust you. After that **you** will never need to fear even if deaths do occur."

Two years passed without a single death in the hospital.

◑

I shall never forget my first surgical patient, the bandit with a bullet in his leg. As soon as I set eyes on this big brute of a man, who was evidently accustomed to being in brawls with firearms, I was convinced that he was one of those dangerous outlaws that Governor Ts'ên was trying to root out from along the borders of the province.

Huang limped in one forenoon, his right leg swollen and red, and told us a fanciful story of how he and his companions had been set upon by robbers while walking peacefully along from Liuyang toward the capital. He insisted that they were crossing the mountain range a hundred li to the east when the robbers attacked them, killing two and injuring several more. Huang had escaped by falling flat when the first shots were fired and by lying motionless so that the attackers believed him dead.

The bandit said that he had received first-aid treatment of a sort in one of the villages near Changsha, "but it was a small village and I am afraid the innkeeper there didn't use the right sort of plaster to draw out the bullet," he added.

I knew about those local venders of plasters who sealed up every sort of abscess or deep wound with a strong-smelling black ointment. I was certain, of course, that the bullet had not left its deep hiding place, so I agreed to go after it. There was no surgical risk involved, but my difficulty was practical: I had neither trained nurse nor anesthetist. T'ou Sz-fu was out of the question as assistant—I was sure he would faint at the first whiff of the anesthetic. Fortunately, an Irish surgeon had

just reached town, on his way to the south of the province. I
went over to the Street of Happy Congratulations and corralled
him for our emergency.

"Do let me use chloroform," he said. "I have never given
ether." This young Edinburgh medical graduate was, of course,
a faithful follower of Sir James Young Simpson who had established the Scottish school of anesthesia in 1847.

We had only a little chloroform in the storeroom and a very
few instruments. Behind the first courtyard was a small room
that had just been whitewashed and would do for the operation.
I explained to my assistant that we had not fitted up a place for
operative work because we scarcely expected to be called on for
surgery so soon. The operating table was an old door, which we
unhinged from one side of the former reception room of the
Central Inn. We laid it across some packing boxes and, presto!
everything was ready for action.

Happily for our reputation, the operation was entirely successful. We found an old-fashioned iron bullet, the sort commonly used in China for centuries. Beyond a trace of rust, it
left no sign of its presence in the wound. I wondered who was
more surprised, the patient at finding himself so painlessly rid
of the bullet, or the public outside when it heard of the "magic
cure." Many a fascinated group gathered around T'ou Sz-fu
during the next few weeks to see the bullet, which we let him
exhibit to everybody.

One day when the bandit himself was seated in the dispensary waiting for a dressing, he became the center of a curious
crowd which pressed him to tell them what had happened.
"The doctor lifted me up on a table and dropped some sweet-
smelling medicine on a cloth that covered my nose. I soon went
to sleep and the doctor cut-with-the-knife. Out came the bullet
from my leg without my feeling any pain at all!"

The bandit became a warm friend. For two weeks after his

Ricefields Stretching into the Distance as far as the Eye Can See

The Powerful Water Buffalo Pulling a Heavy Plow through a Muddy Field

Eyes for Safe Navigation

discharge he came daily to the dispensary to have the incision examined. He wanted to be sure that every particle of the bullet was out. He was afraid that government soldiers would track him down and examine him. If they found a scar on his leg they would say their guns had inflicted the wound. Huang wanted to be careful.

By the time the scar had become practically invisible, he expressed himself as being completely free from fear. "Now I no longer hang up my heart. I have put it down ten parts!" One day he vanished entirely. We could not foresee that, three years later, we should be greatly in his debt.

When I reported the operation at the governor's yamen, I wondered whether I should be reprimanded for having disturbed the peace. The officials told me that this was one of the most notorious criminals in the province and that, when he and his comrades found themselves surrounded by the governor's bodyguard, they had all taken to their heels. No wonder our patient's bullet was found in the back of his leg!

Before long, we had another unusual surgical patient, a Mrs. Chang, who was brought to the hospital by her husband. Both were scholars, thoroughly versed in the medical classics of China as well as in the teachings of the ancient sages. There were few women who knew the Chinese classics as did Mrs. Chang.

His wife, Mr. Chang explained, had long suffered from a wound in the lower abdomen, a wound that would not heal, although he had consulted the best doctors in Changsha, men who conformed to the old Chinese tradition that

The physic of a doctor in whose family medicine has not been practised for three generations at least should not be taken.

He asked me to examine Mrs. Chang and determine whether I could guarantee a cure. "You know our custom with a new doctor," he explained. "We always try to insist that he *pao chên*—guarantee recovery."

Mrs. Chang entered the hospital for observation, and we searched everywhere for the source of the discharge. One morning, she suggested that she might be able to throw light on the picture. She handed me a little pencil sketch, one of the treasures I have kept through the years as an evidence of the keenness of thoughtful Chinese for a correct diagnosis. Even this bit of a sketch seemed to illustrate the truth laid down by Confucius more than four hundred years before Christ:

Look to see where it starts!

Above the pencil drawing, which was a rude anatomical sketch, were these words: "My illness has four roots; one in the kidney, one in the groin, one in the lower vertebrae, and one in the intestine. Please determine, sir, which of these four roots is the ultimate cause of my trouble. You are so busy during rounds that I don't have time to explain it to you." Mrs. Chang had, undoubtedly, just about exhausted the possible sources of the discharge.

I never saw a more concerned or attentive husband than Mr. Chang. After his evening visit he would sit by me in the tiny office and tell me how well read his wife was, that she knew the writings of the philosophers of China, as well as of the historians and the famous medical men. "She can tell you about the great writers in medicine," he explained, "in all the different fields. The other night I found her reading a book on diet and nutrition written in the reign of Wan Li, one of the emperors of the Mongol Dynasty. Ever since discovering that book, she has tried to regulate her diet so that no harm shall come to this wretched wound of hers."

Dr. Hou and I operated in several stages, and gained ground each time. Unhappily, after the fourth operation, relatives came to call, bringing sweetmeats of which Mrs. Chang was very fond. She not only overate, but sat up to entertain the guests, only twenty-four hours after the delicate intestinal operation. Her husband told me on the morning after her death that she was certain all along that the fourth root in her diagram, the one in the intestine, was the source of her trouble. If she had followed to the letter the instructions in her book on dietetics, he believed, she would probably have lived. There was not a word of reproach or suggestion that the foreign doctor had been unwise in his surgical treatment.

For years Mr. Chang was a regular visitor at the hospital, always asking about the sort of patients we were treating, inquiring whether we had seen another patient with a malady like his wife's. "You will seldom come across a patient," he assured me, "who can draw a picture of her own anatomy and help the doctor find the deep roots of her trouble."

VIII
MEDICAL RIVALS

The doctor (belongs with)
The soothsayer,
The astrologer,
The physiognomist.

WE DISCOVERED "The Red-haired General" quite accidentally one day when we were out for a stroll along the top of the south wall of Changsha. Our children, who enjoyed riding together in their light sedan chair through the narrow streets and up to the great tower at the southeast corner, the *T'ien Hsin Ko*, The Chamber of Heaven's Heart, climbed the steps to the upper story for their favorite view of the city and river.

The whole walled city lay spread out before us, and, beyond it, like a broad band of pale yellow silk, the Hsiang River curved off to the northwest, where it disappeared through a break in a line of dark wooded hills. Across the river stood Yolu Shan, covered with a mantle of deep pink. The azaleas were in full bloom.

We often said, as we walked along the top of the great fortification, that people in America would never in the world be able to picture a wall like this—ten miles round the city, forty feet high, wide enough on top for three automobiles to drive abreast, hemming in—or protecting, if you thought of it that way—the city's population of three hundred thousand.

At eight points in the perimeter, gates pierced the wall to let the floods of human traffic pour through. Steps led up to the top on both sides of each of these great doorways. We could usually persuade the armed guards to turn a key in the lock and let us pass through the barriers to climb to the top of the wall.

Sometimes we met city boys up there flying their long-tailed kites that looked like centipedes or dragons. Usually the only others we met were groups of Hunan soldiers who often drilled there. It was their home ground; we saw them walking, bathing behind matting screens, and watching the "foreigners." We, not they, were the exotic beings there.

On this day we climbed the steps at the South Gate and walked westward. Within a quarter of a mile we came unexpectedly upon an old deserted cannon with a huge dent in the muzzle where a fragment had been shot away. It reminded us of the cannon on a New England village green, except that it was under a mat shed. Incense and lighted candles surrounded it, and the mat shed was hung with scrolls carrying messages of thanks from grateful patients. As we came closer we saw that much of the main body of the cannon was plastered over with red paper. Why all these signs of worship, we wondered. Presently we asked a Hunan soldier who sauntered by.

"That is no ordinary cannon," he told us. "That is the *Hung Mao Chiang Chun*—the Red-haired General."

In answer to our questioning he told us how the cannon became a general. Sixty years earlier Governor Lo of Changsha
paid no attention to the powerful army of Taiping Rebels who
were moving rapidly down the river valley from the south of
the province. The chief of the rebel commanders, who called
himself *T'ien Wang*, the Heavenly King, stationed two regi-
ments of his army outside the wall toward the river and laid
siege to the city for eighty-one days. Twice his soldiers bur-
rowed underground and exploded huge mines under the city
wall, one near the South Gate, where we had just climbed the
steps, and one a bit farther east, near the tower of T'ien
Hsin Ko.

The citizens rushed to fill the breaches in the wall. Squads
of men hurried to the coffin shops which were always stacked
from floor to ceiling with big heavy wooden coffins. They carried hundreds of coffins out to the south wall and filled up the
gaps so fast and so completely that the enemy never realized
the breaches were wide enough for an army to march through.

One day the attacking divisions charged in a great mass below the wall where we were standing, but the Hunan troops
defending this section were ready for them. Just as the enemy
came within easy range, this cannon was fired. That single
shot killed the general, his troops fled in confusion, and the
city was saved.

The grateful citizens named the cannon the Red-haired General after Dutch invaders whom the Chinese called "the red-
haired ones." Whenever the Dutch attacked the coast to gain
trading privileges they fought not with ordinary guns but with
great cannon, and their aim was deadly.

The Red-haired General was venerated by the citizens of
Changsha not only because of his accuracy but because he
sacrificed a part of himself when the shot was fired. The spirit

within him was willing to give a part of its body in order to save the city.

"You see, sir," explained the soldier, "all of us believe there is a spirit in every rock and tree, in every mountain and hill and river. We believe there are protecting spirits even in our guns and swords. Isn't it natural that the people should come up here to worship—not the metal body of the gun, but the spirit within?"

"Do you think the Red-haired General has special powers of protection?" I asked.

"Oh, yes, sir! The women in the city all believe that if the general was strong enough to save the city with a single shot his spirit must be strong enough to save the lives of sick children. You will often see them coming up here in crowds to ask the aid of the spirit. He is strongest when children are seriously ill. Winter or summer, it makes no difference. You would be amazed to see what faith they have in the spirit of the Red-haired General."

I realized that afternoon what a powerful professional rival I had discovered, here in this ancient city: a pediatrician whom the city's mothers had been trusting for over half a century. The young American doctor, these women might easily insist, had not given of his own flesh and blood to save the people of their great walled city.

Another rival was the old fortuneteller down at the corner. He borrowed a bit of space, about three feet wide, from the owner of the big cloth shop. It was good luck to have in front of one's place someone who could consult the oracles and tell human beings how to order their ways.

If the father of a family was sick, a son or a daughter would walk down to consult the fortuneteller, paying a few coppers.

The year and the hour of the patient's birth were asked and written down on a shiny, lacquered, white slab. No use keeping a permanent record of the interview. When it was all over, the ink characters could easily be wiped off the slab, leaving it ready for the next customer. When did the illness begin, in what season, at what hour of day? Then the consultant, having assembled his data, proceeded to calculate his answer.

While the anxious and dutiful son eagerly watched the writing and the calculations, the old man fetched down from the little shelf above him a tall, black-lacquered vase, containing fifty numbered bamboo tallies like those our gateman used when he registered patients each morning for the dispensary. Shaking the vase gently, he waited till one fell out on the table. Its number was checked with the calculations on the white slab; then a big tome, a storehouse of lore from centuries past, was consulted. Finally, the inquirer was given an answer. "Your father's illness began in the hour of the horse. That is associated with disease of the heart. I have consulted the books of wisdom that contain the teachings of the sages. Your father is, indeed, ill with a sickness of the heart. You must keep him very quiet. Don't let him be disturbed by wrangling and confusion in the home. It is good that you make frequent sacrifice in the City Temple. Better still, one of you should go on a pilgrimage to *Nan Yo*—the Southern Sacred Peak. Make a vow to go late this summer if your father recovers."

Everyone knew the story of the flower seller of Peking who supported her aged father and could not eat or sleep when he fell ill. Though she did her best for him, he grew no better. One day she heard that an elderly woman, a neighbor, was going on a pilgrimage with some other woman to *T'ai Shan*, the Sacred Mountain.

"If I went," she asked, "would my father be cured?"

"Those who go there and pray sincerely get all that they ask," replied the neighbor.

"How far is it?"

"More than a hundred li."

"And how much is a hundred li?"

"Ninety thousand paces."

The girl made a mental note of these figures, and, every night, while her father was asleep, went out into the yard, holding a lighted stick of incense. There she paced up and down, carefully counting her steps. When unable to move from fatigue, she prostrated herself and said, facing the mountain, "Excuse me for not visiting your temple. I am only a girl and cannot go."

In a fortnight she had walked the ninety thousand paces. Just at that time, pilgrims were flocking to T'ai Shan to venerate the Goddess T'ien Nai Nai (a Taoist deity of the mountain). Rich and poor thronged her temple from cockcrow, for the pilgrim who was the first to burn incense in the morning was more likely to his prayer answered than later comers. On the morning the girl completed her ninety thousand paces, a wealthy palace attendant from Peking occupied the entrance to the temple, determined at all costs that his should be the first stick of incense to be burned that day; but as he entered he saw, to his amazement, an incense stick already smoking in the burner. He angrily questioned the custodian of the temple, who replied, "I had shut the door, and do not know who came before you."

"I shall be here again tomorrow," growled the rich man. "See that you keep the door properly closed this time."

The next morning, long before dawn, the rich man was there, waiting for the door to open. Rushing to the great burner he found a stick of incense already smoldering in it, while the shadowy form of a girl lay prostrate before the altar. At the noise made by the rich man's entrance, the form vanished.

What's this? thought he. Do *Kuei* and *Kuai*—ghosts and goblins—offer incense to this goddess? Going out of the temple he asked the other pilgrims what they thought it could be.

"Ah!" said the elderly woman, neighbor of the flower girl, "this must be the pious florist I know in Peking. As she cannot come to worship in person she has sent her soul to pray for the cure of her aged father."

Still another competitor was a slab of granite that stood near the hospital, facing up the little street that joined the South Gate Main Street. It was four feet by one, and five inches thick, with its back against a rice shop. Any spirit of evil rushing down that lane to enter the main thoroughfare would be stopped in an instant. He could never break into that shop or house, for it was protected by the magic phrase:

T'ai Shan Shih Kan Tang.
The T'ai Shan Stone Dares to Resist.

Everyone knew the Chinese proverb:

Men are three-tenths afraid of devils;
Devils are seven-tenths afraid of men.

Insurance against illness or other ills brought by evil spirits was provided in front! Near by was a consultant who could make direct approach to the gods. There was rarely need of drugs and surgery!

And there were the astrologer and physiognomist who bid for a share of the city's medical practice. The astrologer had volumes beside him in his little street booth. He could tell the name and the place in the heavens of the fate-star of every city. Changsha had a star of its own, Zeta in the constellation

Corvus, the Raven. He knew the influence on life and health of each of the animals in the zodiac and their related constellations. He enlisted the aid of the firmament and the starry host when illness threatened.

The physiognomist, too, might be consulted in an emergency. There always hung charts above his street table with many types of faces depicted. It was necessary for the patient to present himself so that the physiognomist might compare his face, feature by feature, with the standard diagrams. There were little figures or ideographs at each point of the chart, at each corner of the eye; along the nose, the bridge, and the nostrils; and on the mouth, the ears, the cheeks, and the chin. Long training made the consultant skillful in recognizing defects. Those were not only facial lines he sought to recognize, as an artist might scrutinize the features of a sitter, but also points that bore on health. If you knew the lines and points of each chart, you could do much to diagnose your inquirer's malady.

Rivals indeed!

IX

ADVERTISING PAYS

You move your hand and spring returns.

As the weeks passed, we were surprised to find the Yali Hospital receiving attention in the daily press. One day, among the notices about schools, we read:

THANKS TO THE YALI HOSPITAL!

The Yang family, living on Pao Nan Chieh [Precious South Street], have long been concerned about the illness of Grandmother Yang who is seventy years old. They consulted the priests in many temples within the four walls of Changsha, as well as some of the illustrious local physicians, who sought to restore harmony between the conflicting influence of Yin and Yang in her system. Nothing availed, and finally, at the advice of a friend, we took her

to the Yali Hospital on West Archway Street. There the
foreign doctor gave her the cut-knife treatment. She suffered no pain whatever, and is now entirely well. Thanks!
Many thanks!

But the newspapers were not being read by many in 1907.
What was more common, as we discovered when we visited
some of the famous temples, was to find fliers stuck on the
walls outside the gateways, giving thanks for the recovery of
friends. One day I found a group reading a flier that had just
been put up on our front wall. One of our neighbors, the astrologer from the little stand down the street, was reading it aloud
for the crowd: *Yu Ch'iu Pi Ying*—If there is prayer, there is
bound to be response. And, below the printed heading, in ver-
tical lines reading, as always, from right to left, a message of
appreciation as follows:

Our infant son, four years old, had severe bowing of the
the legs and could scarcely walk. Many plasters were
bought for him in the best drug shops of Changsha, and
many diviners and astrologers were consulted. They cast
his horoscope and told us what we should do. We also
visited the city temples and many famous physicians, but
recovery did not follow. Then, somewhat hesitatingly, we
went to see the foreign doctor at the Yali Hospital on West
Archway Street. The doctor told us that the boy needed
lime in his bones and the juice of oranges. After a month
or so of treatment with oranges and medicine, he made the
child stay one whole day without food, then caused him to
smell dream medicine. We stood near by, full of fear. But
the doctor cut-with-the-knife and treated the bones of each
leg, finally sewing up the skin and wrapping each leg in a
stiff bandage. He told us the bandage cloth was full of *shih
kao*, plaster of Paris. We knew that *shih kao* was a harmless
substance, for we use it all the time in preparing the bean

curd that everybody eats. When the child woke up from his sleep, the bandages were as hard as wood. The child experienced no pain, but the doctor gave him some medicine to keep him asleep the first night. In six weeks the stiff bandage was removed, and we found the legs quite straight. The child is now able to walk. Let other parents take notice of this miraculous cure and have their children treated at the Yali Hospital. Gratitude! Gratitude Ten Parts!

It was entirely possible, I thought as I turned away from the group reading the vivid account of a surgical case, that such unsolicited advertising would have been looked upon with suspicion in New York or London. The judicial committee of the local medical society might investigate and give a verdict that there had been unethical practice. But what it achieved in Changsha was a strengthening of people's courage.

Every now and then, with increasing frequency, the gatekeeper would bring in a long visiting card printed on brilliant red paper about ten by four inches, and report to me. "Mr. Li, who lives on *Pei Mên Chêng Chieh*—North Gate Main Street—sends you his card, sir, with the registration fee of five dollars, and asks you to come to his house as soon as possible. The patient is very ill. He has been spitting blood, and the family is quite distracted. Can you go at once, sir? Their family sedan chair is out in the courtyard, waiting for you." I used to wonder how sanitary the inside of such a sedan chair might be, especially when heavy curtains hung down in front of the passenger, and when I felt certain that more than one in the family was likely to be spitting blood. But such professional calls were seldom refused. Each one meant entry to one more home.

On one occasion, the consultation had nothing to do with acute illness. As soon as I sat down in the guest hall of this well-to-do merchant's home and tea had been served, the host proceeded to ask whether anything could be done to insure his wife's having a baby. His story was one we heard frequently:

The *t'ai-t'ai* (ranking wife) had never conceived, though they had been married for ten years. What could they do? Was the merchant to go on childless to old age? If he did not beget a son, there would be no one to carry on the family tradition and to worship regularly before the ancestral tablets when he died, just as he had worshiped at the shrine where the tablets of his parents and grandparents stood. A year earlier a friend, the rice merchant who lived next door, had agreed to act as middleman and to find a concubine, a strong young woman of good family. The merchant inquired and found that her married brothers and sisters all had children. But now she had lived in his house for nearly a year, and had not yet conceived. Both the merchant and his wife were puzzled. "If only you could help us, sir," promised the merchant, "it would be known all through Hunan province, and everyone would say that you were a worker of miracles."

He reminded me of the teaching of the sages that the fundamental requirements for an enduring civilization were filial sons and daughters.

> There are three unfilial acts.
> The greatest is to have no posterity.

No wonder they consulted us when fertility appeared to be threatened!

I examined the husband and the concubine, who was brought to the hospital and studied carefully. She was put on a special diet, given other hygienic instructions, and told to report every few weeks. The result was better than I had dared to hope. When she finally bore a son, the grateful husband almost overwhelmed me with appreciation. More serious still, our hospital became a mecca for women who had remained childless. They told us that they had been to the temple of the Goddess of Mercy over and over again, and the priests had advised them, when nothing else availed, to go and see the foreign doctor.

Calls for professional visits to various parts of the city began to increase. We soon learned which were the better residential streets and what was the standing of those great personages to whose homes entrance grew more and more frequent; where this distinguished gentleman had been *taotai*, and in what provinces that other one had been governor. Visits like these taught me that official appointment in China was dependent solely upon high standing in the district, the provincial, or the metropolitan examinations. Anyone who could qualify on the basis of his results in these grueling tests was eligible for appointment as district magistrate or even for the higher posts of governor or viceroy. The strength of China's official system lay in the democratic way of selection to which everyone submitted. Nor could anyone serve as an official, minor or major, in his own province. That would make nepotism possible. Too much pressure might be made in Peking if a man was of the soil. Changsha, I found, was like every other capital. Its men of influence were of two sorts: those from other provinces who were appointed to official posts, and members of the local landed gentry.

Often our advertising was direct, by word of mouth. I began to grow bolder, now and then stopping a man with a particularly wide-open harelip on the street.

"Good morning, my friend! What is your honorable name? Wouldn't you like to have that cleft in your upper lip completely eliminated? If you will come to the Yali Hospital for a few days, we can set it right for you."

"Can you guarantee a cure, sir? How long will it take? Is it necessary to live in the hospital? How much will it cost?" Perfectly natural questions, and the answers I gave proved, in an increasing number of cases, to be acceptable.

From then on, we had an epidemic of harelips. More and more often people would say to me, when they met me on the street or at some official gathering, "You are making a great reputation, sir, as an external disease doctor. However, we do not believe that the medicines prescribed by the Western doctors for internal diseases will prove as effective as those of our Chinese doctors."

As I now think back to that frankly uttered judgment, I am sure it is safe to say that, even after twenty-five years in China, this was the commonly expressed opinion: "We trust your surgery, but have greater confidence in Chinese medicine."

Scarcely had the Yali Hospital established its reputation for curing harelips when eye diseases began to present themselves. Very little advertising was needed, once I got started.

I was grateful enough for the experience with cataract operations at Miraj in India, for now I had to deal with a perfect spate of them, some immature, many inoperable. Most of them had been needled already by men with dirty hands. On the whole, however, the cataract cases were less troublesome than those coming in from the villages with glaucoma or, even more often, with huge opacities covering the cornea, the result of untreated infections. Some of the poor patients that came to the dispensary looked as if they hadn't had adequate nourishment for years. I soon made up my mind to follow the advice of the great Chinese food expert, Hu Se-hui, who said (A.D. 1330): "When you see a seriously ill patient, think first of his dietary needs; when these have been attended to, he may be given appropriate medication." I soon found, especially in surgical conditions, that the patient's nutrition was the deciding factor in his recovery.

Our best advertising was the people who went home. They would gather their friends about them when they reached their villages, often hundreds of li from Changsha, and tell them all about the details of their life in the hospital, the arrangements for sleeping and eating and all that, but especially about the central theme of their stay there: the operating room, the anesthetic, and the cut-with-the-knife doctor.

Many a patient was terrified at seeing the doctor and his assistant completely clothed in white robes, usually of un-bleached material. White was the color of mourning and un-bleached white cotton garments were the costumes of mourn-ers. One peasant woman, persuaded against her better judgment to come to the hospital where the cut-with-the-knife doctor practised, had not been warned about the sights in an operating room. She was wheeled in on a stretcher and placed carefully on the operating table. While straps were being adjusted about her, she opened her eyes, leaped off the table, and ran scream-ing down the corridor to her bed in the ward. "I knew I should die if I went to the foreigner's hospital. Then when I saw the mourners round me, I knew that I was on the way to my own funeral."

Nor was that all. When she got back to the village, her courage having been finally restored so that she underwent the needed pelvic operation, she told her friends about the medicine they gave her at night. "The attendant would put a little white pill into my mouth and tell me to wash it down with a swallow of tea, saying it would put me right to sleep. But you may be sure, just as soon as she left my bedside, I would spit it out. Who knew whether that attendant, dressed in a mourning robe, wasn't just another one preparing for my funeral, and wasn't giving me some poison medicine to make sure I didn't remain alive?"

One day Gatekeeper Chou stopped an elderly, feeble, stooped countryman as he came in from the street. "Let me see what you have in that bundle. It is a rule of the hospital that all bundles are to be examined, coming in and going out."

Gazing round with some concern, the patient bent over and asked the gatekeeper to come and stand close to him. Unwrapping the bundle, he brought to light a huge tumor that was attached to the inner side of the left thigh. The patient had heard, out there in the country, that growths like this could be removed on West Archway Street at the Yali Hospital. "And you will feel no pain at all," knowing ones had told him.

I asked him to tell me how the growth had started.

He began in a hesitant manner, telling me that, twenty years before, he had been a famous fighter. He had ridden in the cavalry in the war between China and France, down on the coast in Fukien province. One day a bullet wounded him severely on the left thigh. He fell from his horse and bled badly until, after several hours, he was found by some French orderlies. They took him to the French field hospital where he was stitched up and carefully bandaged. When peace was made at the end of that French War, he was released and made his way back to Hunan. After a time the lump began to grow, until about five years earlier it had reached its present size. He had often wished for the French doctors who took such good care of him.

"One day last month," he concluded, "they told me there was another foreign doctor in Changsha, an American. I didn't know anything about you, sir, but I felt sure you would be as skillful and as kind as those French doctors. Is it true that you can cut-with-the-knife without letting me feel any pain?"

I assured him that the removal of the tumor would not endanger his life and that it could be taken off painlessly. It was attached to the thigh by a long pedicle of skin and subcutaneous tissue. I only wished Jim Mitchell, my surgical coach at Johns Hopkins, could have done the operation. I had never seen anyone so skillful with local anesthesia.

Fortunately we had a good supply of clamps. The growth was full of big vessels. If they had bled badly our patient would have needed some sort of transfusion. But everything went well, the wound healed rapidly, and, in a week, the man started for home.

"I am going to put that big tumor in alcohol and keep it in a large glass jar," I said to him as he bade me goodbye, "so as to reassure other people who come in to me with big growths like this one."

"Oh, no, sir! I couldn't possibly let you keep it here. It must go back to the village with me and be buried with me when death comes. That tumor is truly part of me, sir!"

I lost a museum specimen that day, but I gained a friend. The old veteran spread the news about our hospital up and down the province. He had it written up in flowery language in the chief provincial newspaper, and ascribed to the foreign doctors all the powers of the famous surgeons of old China. He said that, while China's physicians were distinguished, it was these foreign surgeons who knew what to do with things that had to be cut-with-the-knife.

Best of all, the reaction down in the country reached back into the capital, even to our own West Archway Street. People high and low were more friendly. They were beginning to understand!

X

"I HAVE COME TO THANK YOU, SIR!"

謀在人成在天

To plan rests with man;
To complete rests with heaven.

No DEATHS in the Yali Hospital for two years! But who could be satisfied with such a negative report? True, we had been doing harelips and cataracts, had opened many abscesses, had done a good many simple plastic operations, but no major cases had been attempted. The faculty at the Yali Preparatory School were relieved that we were so careful. Any attack on the Yali Hospital would surely bring them disaster as well.

Clearly, if this merely cautious advance, this unwillingness to take the chance of danger while fighting to save life, were to continue, we should be no whit different in our attack on disease from the many local Chinese doctors who always insisted on playing safe. No, we must be bolder.

One day, a very sick boy was brought in from a village not far away. He had a discharging wound in the thigh and the family begged for an operation. "Please, sir, cut-with-the-knife. We have heard in our village that you can perform miracles."

But even a miracle worker was bound to hesitate with a patient in such a desperate condition. Besides, was the time yet ripe to risk a fatal result in a surgical case? I remembered how Teacher Liu had told me, two years earlier, that every Chinese thought of the body as the abode of the invisible spirit. Cutting the body would be like defacing the image handed down by one's ancestors, like inflicting a permanent wound on the dwelling place of the spirit.

But today the family was impatient for action. They readily agreed to sign a release. "It will be our responsibility if anything unforeseen happens. He will die if you don't operate. You may be able to save him."

I agreed to explore. The operation was brief, merely providing adequate drainage; but the boy's system was permeated with poison. The shock of the operation was too much for him. He died three hours later.

Fortunately, our Chinese surgeon knew the mental reactions of his countrymen. I turned to him with assurance. We went off alone to the hospital office to lay out a plan of action.

"Do you realize," he asked me, "what a critical day this is for our hospital? Never before has a Chinese patient died in the province of Hunan under the care of a foreign doctor."

Then his manner changed from apprehension to insistence. "Send your official card to the governor at his yamen without delay. Ask him to station a few soldiers from his personal body-guard at the hospital. Then go home, get your lunch, and let me see what I can do."

It was a tremendous relief to have him make these sugges-tions, which I followed promptly.

The soldiers were soon sent down by Governor Ts'ên and stood on guard in front of the hospital until late into the night. Another squad was sent to South Gate Street to reinforce the little group of soldiers who had, from the beginning of our stay in Changsha, occupied a small room immediately oppo-site our own front gate. I sent a note to my family telling them under no condition to go out of the house. Similar messages were sent to the American families of the Yali School faculty. Then, somewhat unhappy, I made my way home.

As soon as I left the hospital, Dr. Hou asked what the fam-ily would be able to spend, at the very outside limit, for a coffin. He found that they were poor farmers and would never be able to spend over ten silver dollars, so he sent the hospital steward out on the street and told him to spend twice that amount. Even this would come to only six American dollars. Could so small an outlay help us out of our dilemma?

Then he had the body prepared and laid in the coffin exactly as he knew the family would wish it.

Walking back after lunch, I was still restless, going over the situation in a kind of inner debate, fully aware that deep re-sentment might break out. These Hunan people were so con-servative, so proud, so confident of the complete adequacy of their own medical practice. What would they do?

And yet death was bound to come some time. Might we not as well face it now? The dilemma was a real one, for every town in the province was in intimate touch with Changsha, the capital city. Within a few days, every farmer, even in the most remote district, would be sure to hear that the son of Farmer Li of Changsha had died in the Yali Hospital after an operation by an American doctor. What would the father and the family do? Would they start a riot in our street? Would we have to close the hospital and admit that Hunan was not yet ready for Western medicine? All these thoughts crowded into my mind as I returned to the hospital.

The governor's soldiers stood in a row at the front gate, tense, expressionless. No word was exchanged between us. Even the gatekeeper looked anxious, almost alarmed, as I passed his door.

Dr. Hou met me at the office quietly. "*Fang hsin!*—Set your heart down! I hope there will be no trouble. Now if the boy's father doesn't make an outcry . . ." Just then the gatekeeper hurried in and whispered something to him.

"The father has come and has examined the coffin carefully," Dr. Hou told me, "but will not open his mouth to say a single word, except that he asked how much we paid for the coffin."

Dr. Hou excused himself and disappeared. The next ten minutes were anxious ones as we wondered how he was faring with the father. But we heard no loud language. The servants went about their hospital duties without making a sound.

Presently Dr. Hou came to the office. "The boy's father is seated in the guest hall. You should go there and receive him." He did not accompany me, for he believed there was less likely to be trouble if I saw the man alone.

"Any Chinese citizen," he assured me, "will try to be courteous to one he is meeting for the first time."

Imagine the pounding of my heart as I stepped over that threshold! At the other end of the hall stood Farmer Li, erect, dressed in a long, plain, blue cotton gown, his face full of deep sorrow, but without any sign of yielding to his inner emotion.

Seeing me enter, he knelt down respectfully, and kotowed three times. I begged him to rise and sit with me on the ceremonial settee at the top of the room. While still standing, he said, very quietly, "I have come to thank you, sir!"

I had expected an angry outburst.

"You have provided for my dead boy a coffin far more costly than we poor people in the country could ever have afforded. For the boy to die was the will of Heaven; but you, sir, have been a friend. I have discovered today how truly our great sage Confucius spoke when he said:

> Within the four seas
> All men are brothers.

I shall return to the village and tell all the people there that you are truly our friend and that we can trust you and your hospital fully."

From that day on, we had no fear of death. The hospital mortality rate began to rise slowly. The townspeople were ready, at last, to let some of their dangerously ill cases be brought to us.

XI

THE HOLLOW NEEDLE
MEDICINE

熟讀王叔和
不如臨症多

To read the medical classics exhaustively
Is not equal to frequent visits to the sick.

MADAME T'AO brought her daughter over to the hospital on a
special stretcher that had been improvised. "We want to put
the girl in your care. All the best Chinese doctors in Changsha
have prescribed for her, yet she does not get better." The
mother realized how seriously ill the girl was and had decided
to ask me to treat her in the hospital.

She was ill indeed. Typhoid fever, with a high temperature
and delirium—a very gloomy outlook. I gave each of the others

in the immediate family a shot of typhoid vaccine, then went ahead with the care of the eighteen-year-old patient, using cooling baths as Osler had taught us. I thought it was a thoroughly modern procedure. Madame T'ao asked me the next day whether I had ever heard of Dr. Chang, one of the most renowned of China's old physicians and at one time mayor of Changsha. "Your use of enemas and of cooling baths reminds me of what my father used to tell me of this celebrated physician's way of treatment. Tomorrow I will bring over, for you to see, one of the volumes of the remarkable essays this old-time physician wrote."

The following morning Madame T'ao brought over the first volume of *A Treatise on Typhoid Fever*, by Chang Chung-ching, published about A.D. 196. It was an astounding discovery to find such a book in Changsha. Here were accurate descriptions of the onset of the fever: chilliness and headache; loss of appetite and nosebleed; temperature rising higher each afternoon. Osler could scarcely have given a clearer picture. More important still, old Dr. Chang had written, "Never use drastic purgatives in this fever. If necessary, use enemas of pig's bile, mixed with a little vinegar, and inserted with a slender bamboo tube. If the fever is high, use cooling baths; they will be found to give strength to the patient and reduce his delirium."

Madame T'ao told me more about this historic book, written in Changsha, where our hospital was supposed to be setting the pace in scientific diagnosis and treatment. Her father, who was always reading biographies, especially of the eminent medical men of China, was particularly devoted to this celebrated physician and considered these volumes the first rational treatise on treatment ever written in China.

He thought one reason for the fame of the book was its classic style, something all Chinese literati admired, and insisted that this *Treatise on Typhoid Fever* was in every sense the medical

equivalent of *The Four Books,* which formed the foundation
of the Confucian classical literature. In her father's library, she
said, were several editions, the best being one published during
the Sung Dynasty. It was in fourteen volumes and contained
two hundred and ninety-seven outlines of treatment and over
a hundred prescriptions.

Dr. Chang, who received his literary degree during the reign
of the Emperor Ling Ti of the Han Dynasty, became interested in typhoid fever when he saw that most of the deaths
in his native village over a period of ten years were from this
disease. In that time the deaths numbered two-thirds of the two
hundred inhabitants. One epidemic so impressed him by its
severity that he gave himself over to the study of the causes and
symptoms, the treatment and prevention of the disease. A
Treatise on Typhoid Fever was the result.

Repeated editions of Chang's great work had been issued
through the centuries, Madame T'ao told me, and with many
commentaries. One of the first of these was by Dr. Wang Shu-
ho, China's great authority on the pulse, who lived a century
or so after Dr. Chang.

From then on, I found that every intelligent Chinese knew
about this book. I soon concluded that far more people in
China knew about Dr. Chang and his work on typhoid fever
than did my countrymen about William Osler and other physicians who had described this fever.

During the next few days, as I cared for Madame T'ao's
daughter, I felt as if I were listening to the voices of two
counselors. Both of them seemed to warn me about symptoms
that might appear toward the end of the second week, or a
sign that might be peculiarly unfavorable. These two distinguished physicians lived seventeen hundred years apart and in
opposite hemispheres; yet each possessed something that put
him ahead of most of his contemporaries. It was fascinating to

discover how many similarities there were between the two. Both emphasized the prime importance of diagnosis; both were bedside clinicians, experienced in interpreting symptoms; both were different from their contemporaries in cautioning against excessive medication and in recommending hydrotherapy. How near together these two great leaders were, though continents and centuries apart!

On the fifteenth day of her illness, the patient's condition became grave. I took Madame T'ao aside and told her frankly how ill her daughter was. Could we take the chance of death in the hospital for a member of such an influential family, whom no expensive coffin could comfort as it had Farmer Li? I hoped she would make the move.

"You can make your daughter more comfortable if you take her home. You see, we have a very ordinary building here. Some day we shall have a beautiful new hospital, with well-trained nurses. But at present the rooms in this old building are really very bare and inadequate. If you decide to take her home, I shall do all I can for her and shall see to it that the same treatment is continued there."

The mother understood what I meant, of course; she must have sensed my anxiety. But mothers never give up. "Please try the hollow needle medicine for another day. Let us confer again tomorrow."

Somewhat doubtful as to whether the girl would last through the night, I consented. Strychnine and digitalis kept the flickering flame alive through the hours of the night; by morning, I saw what lay ahead.

"Madame T'ao, I think it is clear that you would be wise to take her home now."

Somewhat agitated, she asked, "Can we get her home in time?"

"I am sure we can."

A mattress was brought to the side of the patient's bed. I lifted the frail body and laid it gently on the stretcher, our only ambulance. Against the feet, the hands, and the abdomen, I placed hot-water bottles. Then the stretcher cover was fastened on, three hypodermics were loaded with strychnine, and off we started through the narrow streets of old Changsha. Two bearers carried the stretcher; I walked alongside; immediately behind was the mother in a sedan chair and, following her, the younger daughter in another chair.

It was a strange sight for bystanders and shopkeepers to see us rushing through that crowded thoroughfare. Doctors in China were not supposed to be seen walking to consultations, but here was the strange foreign doctor walking beside a covered stretcher. They wondered what might be inside. People stared at us, shuddered, and shook their heads doubtfully. Mothers held their little children behind them.

Death was racing us through those winding streets. Which would reach the old mansion first? Even the bearers knew they would not be allowed to pass through the gate of the house unless the patient was alive. As we came out on one of the city's squares, I stopped, signaled to the mother, and gave the patient a hypodermic. The mother nodded approval. She still trusted the hollow needle medicine, even though with a sort of forlorn confidence. We raced on, coming presently to a wider part of the street. The cavalcade stopped again, Madame T'ao nodded once more, and I gave the patient a second hypodermic. In about twenty minutes we reached the fashionable residential quarter of the old city, and came in sight of the T'ao mansion.

My hopes rose. At the residence, the bearers carried the stretcher up the broad steps, and, to my relief, I saw the big gates thrown open. Just as we reached the platform at the top of the steps, however, a little old woman came out and ordered, "Put the stretcher down!"

My spirits fell. I feared we were to be stalled right there at the gate. There could be no reunion of her spirit with the spirits of the family if death should occur outside the home. The old woman had been the girl's nurse for sixteen years and evidently had the authority to make the vital decision now. She came right up to me. "Is Young Sister still alive?"

The old nurse didn't wait for me to answer. She threw back the stretcher cover, felt of the patient, and rose, smiling. "Take her inside. I have felt her body. She is still warm and truly alive!"

The bearers passed through the great ornamented gateway. We had gotten her home, but had we won the race with death? Back farther and farther they carried the stretcher, until we reached the women's apartments. There the bearers took her into a darkened room, laid the stretcher on the floor, then hurried away. As my eyes grew accustomed to the dim light, I could see that the room was filled with seated women. Presently the mother and sister came in, but no one moved to lift the girl from the stretcher. They all seemed afraid. Finally I took her young body, laid it on the bed, and turned her face toward the wall. Then, receiving approval from the mother for the third time, I gave the patient the third hypodermic that I had carried all the way from the hospital.

Bowing to the relatives, I quietly made my way through the courts and corridors to the front gate. There, just as the doors were closing behind me, I heard an outburst of wailing from the women's apartment.

They had discovered!

XII

OUR HOSPITAL NEIGHBORS

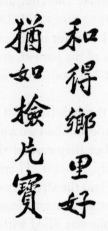

To be on good terms with one's neighbor
Is as good as finding a treasure.

WEST ARCHWAY STREET was a busy, crowded thoroughfare less than a quarter of a mile long and nowhere more than twenty feet wide. Its pavement of granite slabs was like a stage on which, all day long, a fascinating panorama moved.

Water carriers passed with bamboo poles across their shoulders, each pole with two dripping buckets. Most of them brought their load from the river which was only a few hundred yards away. Sometimes they came up through Little West Gate, sometimes through Great West Gate. We could tell just how far it was down to the river by watching the path they

A Pagoda Towering High to Prevent
Misfortune

The T'ai Shan Stone Dares
to Resist

The Gorgeous Dragon Screen in Front
of the Main Gate

Right among Shopkeepers for Neighbors
(Approaching West Archway Street)

left behind them: the wetter their tracks, the nearer we were to the river. We could tell the season of the year, too, by the shade of the water in the big buckets. In winter, when the current was lazy, they carried a clear, clean-looking supply; in summer, when the river often rose six to ten feet in a day, the water in the buckets was a dark, muddy brown, like the raging spate out in midstream.

Another line of water carriers came in from the south side, a second dripping procession. They brought their crystal-clear supply to the Yali Hospital and to homes throughout the city from the "Sand Spring," outside the South Gate. This was by far the best drinking water available to the population of three hundred thousand. The spring flowed ceaselessly, summer and winter, as irrepressible in its stream as Changsha itself was a city unconquerable. People from Changteh, the commercial city ninety miles away, paid a graceful compliment to the provincial capital by calling it

> The City of the Long Sands
> With its Sand Spring,
> The Spring without Sand!

There were other carriers as well: the men with huge loads of rice or beans of a dozen sorts, of sweet potatoes or turnips or cabbages or hsien ts'ai (amaranth), or many another of the vitamin-bearing green vegetables of Hunan. Why should there ever be vitamin deficiency in a province so rich in greens and reds and yellows, the bright colors that we saw everywhere in the vegetable gardens that ringed the city round for miles in every direction? And such loads of peppers! The people of Hunan had always been known for their delight in hot condiments. Flaming red peppers garnished each bowl, and either the scarlet or the milder green peppers flavored each sauce.

And mingled in with the baskets of grains or vegetables was

an interminable procession of other peddlers and venders, each with a bell or gong or rattle that announced his approach and told of the particular wares he had to offer. The seller of china-ware, with a big load of bowls and dishes, always struck a heavy strip of iron that produced a ringing bell-like note. We knew the vender of sweetmeats and cakes was coming when we heard the sound of his tiny tinkling gong. Each was distinctive. Far into the night, when but few lights were left burning on the main streets, we could hear the tinkle-tinkle of the traveling restaurant. Barred gateways and locked shop doors that seemed closed fast for the night would open gently when they heard the vender approaching. The doorkeeper or an old nurse would appear and bargain for some dainty—just a snack for someone in the great house before bedtime. They knew his re-frain as he sold his cakes:

> They cure the deaf and heal the lame,
> Preserve the teeth of the aged dame!

Many others, too, traveled that street: the coolie with his huge load of coal from the Pinghsiang collieries not far from the city pushed along on the stone-paved street a heavy wooden wheelbarrow that carried at least two hundred and fifty pounds. All these carriers of heavy loads, charcoal or firewood or bundles of kindling wood, were a part of that interminable procession. The human loads moved along fairly quietly on bare feet or on feet wearing straw sandals, but there were disturbing sounds as well. We often heard a mixture of squeaks and grunts and roars. When we looked out of the window, we saw a wheel-barrow passing, its axles tortured for want of grease, and strapped to it a huge pig, pink and white all over, bound with heavy ropes, unable to move or withdraw its snout that pro-jected just far enough over the edge of the wheelbarrow to graze each passing ricksha.

Imagine being inside the thin outer wall at the front of the Yali Hospital on a busy morning, assailed by the noise inside made by the turbulent mob of patients waiting for medical attention, and outside, by the clamor of all those passers-by! Imagine trying to listen to some patient's chest in the midst of all that hubbub! At first I thought I could never get accustomed to it, but as time passed I found it possible, even in the midst of the din, to make out heart sounds clearly, just as with boiler riveters who, we are told, learn to sleep inside a cylinder of steel, while huge hammers pound away outside. Even the shallow, rapid breathing of a child could be plainly distinguished with the stethoscope, once the strident sounds outside became merged into a vague hum and the clarity of sense perception was no longer dimmed.

All day long and far into the night, that ceaseless stream rushed on. As time passed, these men and women, carriers of heavy burdens, chair bearers and water coolies, all entered into my consciousness, no longer unknown beings out there at a distance. They became my neighbors, my friends. We were living together, not as native and foreigner, but as fellow citizens, sharing the life of a great metropolis.

But there were other neighbors, too, less visibly mobile; they were the friendly shopkeepers living and working beside me on that narrow street. Shop after shop, like the individual cells along some corridor in a giant honeycomb, had its individual gay signboard. Some were hung across the top of the doorway; others, like tall banners, hung down from decorative midroofs that projected over the street like oriel windows. To the casual passer-by, the entrance to the Yali Hospital must have seemed like just one more of those many gateways, one of the scores on the busy thoroughfare. Looking along both sides of the street, one saw opening after opening, all so much alike. It was a long succession of doorways, some six feet wide, some fifteen, some thirty, all opening inward. Through some you could look into the tiniest room or shop imaginable; through others you caught a glimpse of a large establishment.

Each door was like the frame of a picture, enclosed in which one might see a living scene. It might be a chinaware shop, in which gay bowls seemed even more festive when filled, all winter long, with narcissus bulbs that sent their shoots upward slowly enough to keep the stems strong under each dainty blossom. The Chinese spoke of them as "water fairies." How different from the forced growth of the narcissus in a steam-heated apartment, where the development is too rapid and the flower wilts quickly! In an open Chinese shop, so cold that the seller has to wear heavily padded clothes and ear tabs to keep from freezing, only "fairy blooms" can keep unabated their strength and fragrance.

Sometimes when an outer door would fly open, the passer-by could get a glimpse of a courtyard. In summer one saw rock pools with the glint of flashing goldfish fins. In winter, in the midst of penetrating cold, one became aware of the pervasive fragrance of the winter plum. People always said in China:

> When the mountain winds blow,
> And the snow lies deep on a night of cold,
> Only the winter plum has fragrance that endures.

To the right of the hospital was a grain shop. All day long coolies brought great sacks of unhusked rice to be stored in its huge bins. They came in through one of the west gates, either directly from the cargo junks that were anchored along the bund or from one of the central warehouses on River Street. Each morning the apprentices measured out so many bushels of the unhusked rice and carried them from the storage bins within to the pounding pits at the front of the shop.

These pits were like bowls, nearly three feet across, sunk

into the ground at floor level. Above them, on a massive log framework, leaned the muscular bodies of the pounding men stripped to the waist, summer and winter. They worked at their job all day long and far into the night. Each pounder threw the weight of his body, first on the right foot, then on the left, depressing the pedal whose further tip ended in a stone mallet at least forty pounds in weight. Each time the stone hammer dropped, it carried the husking process that much further along. We could hear that thud from inside the hospital. Like the heavy beat of a bass drum, it punctuated the rhythm of the singsong chant that the pounders droned. They chanted and pounded just so long, for they knew from experience how many strokes it took to husk the rice grains completely. Then the white kernels would be ready for the retailer and for the boilers in the countless kitchens of the city.

Rice was the king of "the five grains" in Hunan province; it was the essential staple in the people's diet. But there were the other grains as well: rye and millet, wheat and kaoliang, and many kinds of beans. Everyone knew that the grain shop, like the hospital, was concerned with maintaining human life. The doctor grew apprehensive about any patient when the family said, "He can't swallow even a mouthful of rice!"

Before long, the owner of that rice shop became one of our best friends. His ten-year-old boy fell one day from a high pile of stored grain down to the stone pavement, breaking his leg. He was brought quickly to the hospital, the leg was set, a plaster bandage applied. His prompt recovery led to the signing of a rice contract with this good neighbor. The agreement was on a monthly basis; and through all the years that we remained his customers, we never once got short weight or found any falsifying of the accounts. It grew into an experience of mutual service. He was our customer as well as we his.

To our left just beyond the paper shop was P'eng the Ironsmith, with his sledge hammers and anvils and forges, and all the other paraphernalia of a light-metal industry. The owner came over quite early to pay his respects, and, of course, to solicit trade. He was soon making all the iron hinges we needed, as well as the iron rods that were built up into Thomas splints. As time went on he fashioned the iron stands for our sterilizers and instrument cabinets. It was a constantly increasing delight to discover the skill of this master artisan. He could make any metallic gadget or turn any shape where the lathe or the forge was needed. Where else, in the later years of warfare against the invaders' armies, could have arisen those streams of ammunition and small arms that fortified the guerrillas in their mobile, attritional warfare, except from the skill of the Chinese ironsmiths?

On one occasion a bit of apparatus, designed for my son's mouth by an eminent orthodontic surgeon in Los Angeles, went wrong. There was something more serious the matter than a loose screw. I had on my library shelf a copy of Dr. Angle's original work on orthodontia, but that did us little good. We sent for Huang Laopan, the hospital contractor, and he took it down to P'eng the Ironsmith on West Archway Street. The gold wires and hooks came back to us perfectly repaired.

Just beyond the ironsmith's was Li, the maker of brass and enamel tobacco smokers' outfits. His front windows were filled with water pipes, those safe, slow-burning contrivances that the Chinese have used for centuries. You scarcely went to a shop in the early days in Changsha, certainly never to make extensive purchases, without having a water pipe offered you, its little cartridge neatly packed with a fresh filling of tobacco, and a tightly rolled paper lighter put into your hands. There was no need of Virginia or Havana tobacco, for the fields of Hunan produced a leaf that would match any of them.

A little way farther west was Liang, the tobacconist. His apprentices, working all day long, shoved huge planes over the tightly compressed bundles of leaf and turned out, by hand, a powder fine enough for snuff or coarse enough for the water pipe. Chou, the gatekeeper, and T'ou Sz-fu, and, later on, our Chinese doctor and pharmacist, all went there to get the supply for their water pipes. Each member of the staff kept one in his room. These pipes were true symbols of unhurried Chinese hospitality. As I watched men smoking them in their leisurely, friendly way, I often wished that friends in the West might discover how speed and tension were often enemies of comradeship. I was learning, day by day, more and more of the many words in the Chinese vocabulary for peace and serenity, for concord and human harmony. Had any other language so many?

There were many other shops besides: those of silversmiths and coppersmiths and goldsmiths, who could turn out the most beautiful wares; and, a little way up West Archway Street, just as we got over into the Street of the Medicine King (perhaps that was the street on which we should have located our hospital when we first started), were the city's best silk shops. There you could buy all the daintily colored figured silks of China, those of Hunan or of Szechwan, or of Chekiang on the eastern seacoast. Near the silk shops, too, were shops displaying cotton goods from all over the world, and still other shops specializing in heavy satin brocades.

And there were still other neighbors. At least every eighth or tenth doorway bore the sign "FOOD SHOP," or "PROVIDER OF WINES," or "CATERER FOR BANQUETS." Restaurants were everywhere, better or poorer in the quality of their food and in their clientele. You could order anything, from a bowl of rice and a dish of vegetables to a banquet of many courses. We never had any trouble serving a Chinese meal in the hospital or at our house. Any one of half a dozen restaurants right at hand could provide, at prices that seemed to us remarkably low, either "convenience meals," where we sat down with a small group of friends, or more formal meals. Everyone ate whatever his economic status allowed: the poor rarely saw meat in any form the year round, and the well-to-do feasted on costly dainties from sea and river and forest. The art of blending flavors and garnishing dishes must have had its origin in China.

Every time we went up West Archway Street we saw, fastened on the walls near the street corners, little bamboo baskets bearing a strip of red or yellow paper inscribed:

> Look with respect and pity
> On paper bearing written characters!

They were receptacles, not for refuse, but for gathering scraps of written or printed paper. Every few days some old man would come along and empty the baskets. He removed every scrap carefully and took it away to burn in a near-by incinerator. Scholarship, we found, was of greater concern than sanitation.

> Whoever rescues a thousand characters from
> Being trodden under foot adds a year to his life.

Now that we had a place on their street, we hoped that we would not remain foreigners in the eyes of our neighbors. We were in a building they knew. The Central Inn had stood there for decades. People from the villages across the river who had business that kept them in the city for a night, or merchants from the south or west of the province who visited the capital to replenish their stocks for the winter, all these, as well as casual travelers coming to Changsha by steam launch or sailboat, or across country by sedan chair, had frequently put up at the Central Inn. It had established a good name for its clean rooms and its reasonable prices. Then, suddenly, illness carried off the owner, and his son had never learned how to manage a hostelry, in spite of years of association with an experienced father. Our neighbors were grateful to us for one thing at least: it was quieter for everybody after the removal of the pigs from the Central Inn. Their early-morning squeals had disturbed both sleep and emotions.

The sense of being foreigners lessened when we began to pay street dues of a dozen different sorts. We paid the street cleaners, who made a pretence of sweeping the pavement with their short, inefficient brooms, and the drain cleaners, who, at long intervals, took up the granite blocks in the center of the highway and poked obstructions from the only sewer that the street possessed. There were quarterly dues for the lamp lighters, who kept weak flames burning in tiny tin lamps filled with bean or peanut oil. Of course we paid a regular subscription to the street guild itself. It was a sort of union for mutual benefit and co-operative action. The city magistrate could summon the guild leaders to reprimand them for breakdowns of lighting or sanitation or discipline, or to inform them that a new rice tax or coal tax was to be imposed. There was no water laid on, so the only water tax was what we paid to the coolies who brought us water from the river or from the "Sand Spring" outside the South Gate. The owner paid all property taxes to the city government.

Then, too, we were always expected to pay the annual tax to the Robbers' Guild! How, otherwise, could we have escaped petty thieving? The hospital was walled in, to be sure, but doors could be burst open, while street windows were no insuperable obstacles for enterprising burglars. Besides, Chou, the doorkeeper, often dozed in the early afternoon, and a really watchful thief might easily wander in to steal instruments or glassware from the dispensary operating room. It was much easier to provide theft insurance by a friendly subscription, each year, to the chief of the Robbers' Guild. He would then be on our side in case anything of value disappeared.

All round us were streets with unforgettable names. There had to be, to match our street, an East Archway Street; but the names we remembered best were those that carried fragrance or symbolism from the daily life:

> The Pool of the Lotus Flower
> The Street of Precious Gifts from the South
> The Street of the Star of Long Life
> The Road of Happy Congratulations
> The Vale of Tenderness and Grace
> The Lane of Daily Renewal

Our neighbors were becoming aware that we respected their customs and celebrated all the festivals and holidays which they regarded as immemorially a part of their community life. We closed our front doorways at night as their customs provided. When darkness fell, the night roundsman of our precinct struck the bamboo cylinder with one beat for the first watch, and called out his assurance and his warning, as he continued to beat out the watches of the night:

> *Chung wei chieh fang! Hsiao hsin huo chu!*
> All you street-guild-neighbors!
> Be careful about fires and candles!

Sometimes he stopped to have a word on his rounds. "Don't mind the bitter cold of winter," he would say. "Never run the risk of fire in this tightly packed street. Partitions within the houses are so flimsy, paper windows so inflammable!"

People everywhere still hesitated to sleep in upper stories. At the very outset they had told us that, in a well-established Chinese house, the gatemen and the menservants might sleep upstairs with impunity but the members of the family regularly slept on the ground floor. They did not wish to offend the spirits of Feng Shui.

I asked Teacher Liu what Feng Shui meant. "Feng Shui," he assured me, "is an old superstition. People believe that the spirits of wind and water will destroy a house that overtops the near-by temple or pagoda. For the present, the hospital should not use any upstairs room that overlooks our neighbors' bedrooms or the temples on that back street. If there were a pagoda near by, towering above them, that would prevent misfortune, but there is none inside the city wall of Changsha."

A pagoda with its seven or nine or eleven stories—always an odd number—was a sort of spirit lightning rod, protecting all who came under its influence. Since there was no pagoda at hand, we determined not to work upstairs at first, certainly not unless we could persuade the temple priests to raise the walls of their sacred enclosure so as to overtop anything we might build. Imagine what the neighbors would have said if our operating room had been upstairs and the hospital had been struck by lightning!

XIII

AMBULANCES OF A DOZEN SORTS

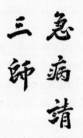

In a critical illness, send for three doctors.

The staffs of hospitals in America or England would have been amused at our unique ambulances. One day, standing in front of the hospital, I saw a coolie come up with the usual bamboo pole across his shoulder, swinging two rice baskets. As he came nearer, I noticed that one of the baskets was filled with crude bedding and old clothes, while in the other sat a child of about four years, with sparkling eyes and a restless face. His mother was walking along beside the bearer, who was the child's father.

I asked whether she had brought her child as a patient. "Yes," she replied, "I have been trying for a long time to bring him to have you 'see his sickness.'" The family, she told me, lived a hundred li to the west, outside of Ninghsiang. This boy was her sixth child; the first five had all died before they were a week old. The mother attributed the deaths to the midwife who was very clever with her hands when the babies were born but who wrapped each baby's cord with something that made it sick. Each infant had fever and went into convulsions.

"What was it she used?" I asked, my suspicions roused.

The mother said the midwife took earth from outside the door of her own house, mixed it with a white powder, and tied it over the cord with a cloth. There was a horse stable next to her house and the woman believed that the earth might have caused the trouble. So many of the babies the midwife brought into the world had died—all in the same way—with convulsions. After the midwife had been in the town ten years, some of the husbands complained to the magistrate. He finally made her move across the village to a place far away from the stable. After that, the babies she delivered did not die.

The mother had called another midwife for this baby. As soon as she could leave the house, she had taken him over to the big City Temple, paid ten coppers to the priest, and begged him to tell her how to save the boy's life. The husband had carried him there in the rice basket, just as he had brought him to the hospital. The priest asked about the date and the hour of his birth, then told the mother that, just as a big rice basket sheltered the grains of life, so would a basket keep the baby's life safe. He instructed her to use the basket as the child's crib all through his infancy, certainly until he was able to run about, so she kept him in that rice basket and called him "Little Basket Boy."

I picked the child up and held him while I listened to his chest. He had a loud heart murmur and I became worried at once.

The mother, I could see, was growing nervous. "Let me have

him back, sir, and keep him in his basket. I am always uneasy when he is out of it for even a few moments!"

"Bring him up to our children's ward," I suggested. "You never saw such a happy lot of youngsters as are there now. Some of them have lung disease and others have bone weakness. But they are in a sunny room up there and you will see how they enjoy playing together."

She came up, expecting to be firm in her refusal to leave her child in any "foreign hospital," but was won over by the gaiety of the children. "Little Basket Boy's" father took his makeshift ambulance home, while the child stayed with us long enough to become really sturdy.

Another day we watched a procession coming up the street toward the hospital. In the background I could see men with drums and horns, like a band of hired musicians. Usually a procession with music meant a wedding or a funeral. They didn't stop at the hospital, however, but hastened past, carrying, not a sick patient, but an image from a temple in a remote corner of the city. They had hired a splendid sedan chair, like those the officials used, gay with red satin and colored trappings. Seated stiffly inside was the image, as expressionless and cold as a mummy.

Our gatekeeper told me that in a house only two streets away from us there was a very sick child. The family had called in physicians and when there was no improvement had consulted the oracle man and the astrologer. When these did not avail they had sent messengers to the temple of the medicine king, paid a big fee to the priests, engaged this gaudy sedan chair, and were now carrying the image of the god of medicine to the home. They believed he would prove powerful enough to drive out the evil spirits of disease that were preventing the child's recovery.

"Some day, sir," added the gatekeeper, "when they understand more about modern medicine, they won't bother about the image of the god of medicine."

The very next day a group of men came to the front gate carrying a bed with a very ill little patient on it. The bed was a cheap wooden frame with wooden legs and with crossed fiber ropes for the mattress. At the head end I saw the body of a freshly killed rooster. The neck was still bleeding.

This was the same child about whom I had heard the day before. After the medicine god had made his visit, accompanied by drums and firecrackers, the child had grown worse. Other priests were called and advised killing a rooster and putting it by the child's head. "The rooster," they told the family, "is the first living thing to greet the dawn. Just as it puts darkness to flight, so will it drive away sickness from your child."

The rooster was caught and killed, but the child's fever continued to rage. A neighbor broke into the family gathering at that point and insisted that they rush the child over to the "foreign hospital" on the bed just as he was. The "foreign doctor" could work miracles with fevers; only last year he had cured a little nephew of just such a fever.

Despairing, almost hopeless, the father and his brother picked up the rough little bed and came hurrying through the narrow street to us. A single drop of blood from the child's ear gave the clue: it was loaded with malarial parasites. One injection of quinine was given immediately, a couple of doses by mouth later, another injection after twenty-four hours, and the child was on the way to full recovery. The relatives carried the bed-ambulance home empty, with dark stains from the rooster's blood still on the headboard.

Another patient was carried in pickaback by his fellow chair bearer. They had come twenty miles across country, they told me, traveling since six o'clock that morning. Just a mile east of the city the patient had fallen in a faint, entirely collapsed. The villagers had tried all the familiar folk remedies: pinching the skin and muscles of his neck, both sides, till they were black and blue, and repeating the performance on the abdominal wall; they had pried his teeth open and laid a small copper cash on his tongue, then sprayed his face several times with cold water from the teahouse well. Finally, they had forced his teeth apart again, removed the cash from his tongue, and examined it minutely.

"The mouth juice hadn't dissolved away even a tiny speck of the copper," the chair bearer said. "All the village people believed he wouldn't die, so I put him on my back and brought him the two miles to the hospital."

They came in sampans and sailboats, in huge cargo junks and steam launches, by steamer and train and bus—always because someone they knew had been to the hospital and gotten well there. Later, when people began to trust us with their maternity cases, the variety of conveyances was even greater. Women were brought rolled up in mattresses slung by ropes to a pole, in homemade hammocks, on rattan chairs or couches, on doors hurriedly unhinged for the emergency journey. The best part of it was that they always had right of way. When they crept along on the narrow footpath between water-soaked paddy fields and met another team, someone had to turn back to where the path was wider. The bearers with the emergency case always knew some magic signal, and the others gave way.

The sedan chair, whether ornate like an official's or unadorned like the bamboo-framed seat that the farmer used, was the standard conveyance. Teacher Liu told us that the Chinese had been using them for fifteen hundred years. He showed us a picture in an old encyclopedia of a famous poet with "an ailment in his foot," who was carried in a basket hanging from a pole resting on the shoulders of two men. Earlier still, there was a famous writer who rode in a "level-with-the-shoulder conveyance" into the Ku family garden. It was common in those early days for officers of the Grand Secretariat to send for a "shoulder conveyance" to take them to their offices when they were ill. It is recorded that the Sung Emperor Shen-tsung (1068–86) "dealt leniently with Imperial Clansmen, permitting the aged and the ill and those who could not ride horseback to come and go on 'shoulder conveyances.' "

Soon after the revolution of 1911, rickshas became a cheap and favored method of transportation. The first ones had iron tires, the later ones solid rubber, and, finally, the new pneumatic tires arrived from Shanghai. Eventually, the motorcar appeared. It was a memorable day when Dr. Yen drove the first tiny car through the narrow thoroughfare of the Street of the Medicine King, down West Archway Street to the bund, and along the bund to where our hospital stood in later years, out in the north suburb. But such innovations came slowly. China's economic status would not permit the motorcar to replace very quickly the ancient two-man team carrying the sedan chair.

One day, out of sheer curiosity I asked the chair bearers of a high official, whom Dr. Hou was treating in the dispensary operating room, where they would go after leaving the hospital. They answered unhesitatingly that they would carry the official to a well-known druggist's shop on East Archway Street. They said their master always sent to this shop prescriptions that his Chinese doctor friends wrote for him. He knew most of the famous doctors of the old school in Changsha and they all patronized the shop.

The following week Dr. Hou took me to the shop on an inspection trip. It was well worth a visit, and, as Dr. Hou reminded me, the city had many more like it. Behind the counter were large drawers for powders and roots and barks. In an alcove at the back we saw an altar to the god of medicine with incense sticks burning on it. There were tribute panels on the walls, glorifying the herbalists of old.

On the shelves stood large blue and white jars containing tonics, such as syrup of pears, to ward off the feebleness of age and to insure easy delivery. I saw the clerks ladling the tonics out of the jars with iron spoons.

In the smaller jars, they told us, they kept seeds and vegetable substances, some of them quite costly. In the drawers there was an odd assortment: *gall bladders of bears* for sore eyes (ten dollars an ounce), the contents of *tiger stomach,* to stop vomiting (four dollars an ounce), *otter livers* for tuberculosis, the *horn of the rhinoceros,* "cures all illnesses" (twenty dollars an ounce), *snake meat,* good for rheumatism. In another set of drawers lay plasters of every sort, some to be applied to the temple, some to other parts of the body.

It was perhaps even more fascinating to get into a sedan chair myself and ride through the narrow streets of old Changsha, looking out for the many little herb shops. Their signs were alluring:

> Hall of the Herbs of Immortality
> Hall of Spring Herbs
> Hall of Ten Thousand Herbs
> Hall of Tranquillity and Remoteness
> Hall of Preserving Harmony
> Hall of the Deep Fountain

To these shops with their poetic names came simple villagers from the countryside, bringing for sale baskets of fresh herbs and roots, whose value was either real or fancied. The poor, afflicted with all the ailments known to the human body, came there and asked the herbalist to prescribe. His bitter concoctions were swallowed in good faith, especially when he followed the age-old rules of his craft.

Dr. Hou and I used to wonder how long it would be before people trusted us as much as they did these herbalists whom they had always known.

XIV

"A PIECE OF JADE"

You have achieved the joy of a jade scepter.

MR. TÊNG came running to our house on *Nan Mên Chêng Chieh,* South Gate Main Street, greatly excited. Instead of letting the gatekeeper go ahead to announce the guest, he insisted on rushing through the long corridors and courtyards to my study at the very back of the property. In one of the court-yards he was in such a hurry to get through that he almost knocked over a great pot in which a splendid camellia bush was in bloom. This was no ceremonial call.

Breathless, he burst into my study in a way that was very offensive to Teacher Liu who was giving me my regular after-noon lesson in Chinese.

"Doctor Hume," he shouted, "please come at once. My wife

is very ill. She is vomiting all the time and is becoming worse
every hour. Please hurry!"

Teacher Liu left the room without a word to the intruder.
I learned later that he went directly to Mr. Têng's father to
report the son's shocking breach of decorum. Young Têng
should really have known better. Perhaps it was his scientific
training in Japan—he had only recently returned—that made
him so careless of the conventionalities taught by the sages.
He was all for chemistry and engineering. Courteous manners,
he often said, were less important in life than science.

"Yes," I replied to the breathless young caller. "I'll go with
you as soon as the gateman can call me a sedan chair."

"Let's walk instead of using those old-fashioned sedan
chairs," he suggested. "We can visit as we walk and I can tell
you about my wife."

So we started off on foot, Li Sz-fu trotting along behind
with my black medicine bag. Mr. Têng explained that his wife
was to have a baby in about seven months. For the past two
weeks she had suffered incessantly from vomiting. She could
keep nothing down, neither solids nor fluids.

"You must be prepared to find her very conservative," he
warned. "All our family follow our Hunan traditions. We have
never had a foreign guest in the home. They tried to prevent
my coming for you."

Presently we reached the cool, spacious house, standing in a
quiet lane off South Gate Main Street. Mr. Têng took me at
once to the patient's bedside. Not only was she in great physical
distress, but the room was crowded, making the atmosphere
insufferable in the summer heat.

Two older women, thorough patricians in carriage and manner, were seated beyond the patient's bed, plainly on guard to
protect the daughter. Mr. Têng introduced me to them. "This
[he indicated the lady in the dark-blue silk gown] is my mother,

and this [he turned to the other lady in the flowered brown silk] is my wife's mother." In English he said to me that they had known each other all their lives and were very happy when their children married. It was plain that they were alarmed.

Both women bowed stiffly when I acknowledged the introduction. Since Mr. Têng and I spoke to each other in English, neither of them knew that I could speak Chinese. I let them remain uninformed, but asked the young man, in English, "Which of the two has the final say in regard to the patient's treatment?"

"Oh, my mother, of course. When a bride comes to her husband's home, his mother becomes her mother and has all the authority. Why, my wife even speaks of her own mother as 'my parent on my mother's side.'"

Every time I moved, the two women watched me. They were the supervisors and I the observed. It was a strange feeling for the doctor to be the center of concern in a sickroom.

What troubled me most was the array of noisy and unintelligent female relatives, who had come in from the country on hearing of the young daughter-in-law's plight. Each of them had some suggestion for altering the treatment that the family had started. Each knew exactly what had brought on the serious situation. In addition, a bevy of women servants surrounded the bed, getting in each other's way, talking incessantly. In an adjoining courtyard Buddhist priests were droning prayers for the sick.

The family had already summoned two of the Chinese physicians who lived near the South Gate. One had ordered a sort of blister to the back. The other had ordered a prescription that had proved potent for centuries, but neither had relieved the young wife.

The husband had assured her, before he went out to call me, that the foreign doctor knew all about modern scientific medicine, and that she must not be frightened when he came; but I knew how apprehensive she was. Either food or medicine, she knew, was bound to be torture. And as to a foreigner! Why should her young modern-minded husband bring him in, when the family all knew she would do better with the local physicians and the well-known herb remedies of Hunan or Szechwan? Her illness was of a sort that Chinese physicians understood. How much better to travel familiar roads than to venture into unknown byways. Her expression said all this very plainly although no word was uttered.

The two mothers came closer to the bedside, listening to me and watching me as a cat watches a cornered mouse. I examined the patient carefully—both pulses, the tongue, the pupils. They brought me a sample of urine, and a test was quickly made. The servants all stood round and stared at the strange procedure. One of them whispered to Mr. Têng's mother that she was sure I was cooking up some decoction which might easily harm the young wife.

When I was sure of the diagnosis I took Mr. Têng into the guest hall and laid the situation before him frankly. "There is only one way, my friend, to save your wife's life; that is to take away the unborn infant. So long as it remains within her, it poisons her whole system. This vomiting is bound to grow worse as the poison spreads. If you trust me, you must let me act at once."

There was a pause as he weighed the proposal. Presently, looking me square in the eyes, he said, "I have every confidence in you. What you say is self-evident. My wife is being poisoned by the unborn life within. Please proceed as you suggest." Then, remembering suddenly that he must consult with others in the family, he added, "Please wait here, sir, till I come back. I shan't be long."

Though no word reached the guest hall from the family conclave that was being held several rooms away, I knew well enough what was being said and was fearful as to the verdict. The guest-hall door opened quietly and the sobered young husband came in. Seating himself in the chair below mine, he spoke with finality.

"Her mother-in-law says NO!"

"In that case, Mr. Têng, you will not mind if I withdraw at once. It is my considered opinion that no other treatment will work. It would waste my time and yours if I should start to treat your wife with drugs."

"I understand perfectly, Doctor Hume. You are very kind to have taken so much trouble for our family today. I will order a sedan chair for you at once."

Just outside the gate, as the sedan chair began to jog along through the winding, crowded street, the bearer nearest me turned, reached his hand back through the curtains, and handed me a bright red envelope, fully ten inches long, heavy with metal. It contained five silver dollars, the regular out-call fee that was charged at our hospital. Mr. Têng had paid his bill and I was completely free from further responsibility. But I thought for days of the young woman's condition, wondering how long she would live.

Four weeks later, on a hot summer day, walking along South Gate Main Street, I caught sight of Mr. Têng in the crowd, cool and unflustered. His long light blue silk gown made my clothes feel oppressive by comparison.

I mustn't meet him. It would be harrowing to hear the details of her continued suffering and . . .

I turned off into a little alley, at right angles to the main thoroughfare, hoping to elude the watchful eyes of my young friend. But I soon heard hurrying footsteps behind me. As he came nearer, he called, "Wait a minute, Doctor Hume. I want to thank you once more for your kindness that day, a month ago, when you took so much trouble for my family. We all appreciated your friendly manner and your professional counsel, even though we didn't follow it."

"Tell me about Mrs. Têng."

"Well, just after you left our home we had another family consultation and decided to summon Doctor Chang to see my wife. He is generally believed to be a descendant of that famous Doctor Chang who was mayor of Changsha back in the period of the Three Kingdoms and is honored everywhere in Hunan for his diagnostic skill and the efficacy of his medicines. We knew that Doctor Chang's fee would be at least twenty taels [about ten dollars United States currency], and that the drugs he ordered would be as costly as jewels, but we determined to have him."

"Did Doctor Chang come?"

"Oh, yes! We sent a special sedan chair to bring him from his residence in Lotus Flower Street, up there inside the city wall near the northeast corner."

I couldn't help smiling as I recalled that I had gone to the Têng house a month earlier—walking! Obviously that had made a poor impression. And my fee had been only five silver dollars—a combination hardly likely to convince a Hunan family.

"Tell me about Doctor Chang's visit."

"He arrived within an hour and found my wife even more wretched than when you saw her. He examined her pulses very carefully, always telling us what had been said by this and that illustrious authority on the pulse. You must know, sir, that for more than sixteen centuries we have followed the teaching of Doctor Wang Shu-ho in interpreting pulse signs. Well, Doctor Chang told us that since this patient's condition was so serious, his fee would be fifty taels. The medicine he prescribed cost at least ten taels a dose, and my wife needed three doses."

"Did it work?" I asked, not expecting to believe.

"Oh, yes, sir! She vomited a little after the first dose, but felt better in spite of it. The vomiting stopped completely after the third dose, and it has never recurred. She can now eat and drink whatever she likes. She is entirely well. I hope for a son six months from now! It will be my first child, you know, and we all say that a son is like a piece of jade."

Six months later, young Mr. Têng made me a ceremonial call. He brought the good news that a son had been born. This time he waited for me in the guest hall. "My wife has presented me with a piece of jade."

She had been perfectly well through all the waiting months. I wondered what potent medicine the Chinese doctor had prescribed.

☯

Another home ruled by a matriarch also bound by tradition was that of Ch'ü T'ai-t'ai. Madame Ch'ü was a great lady, a poet and a painter, and she controlled the management of the family property as well. No one could cheat her regarding the number of bushels of rice yielded by the family fields out in the western villages.

One day this forceful woman fell ill and sent for me. Grand Councilor Ch'ü met me at the great gates, led me back as far as the women's apartments, then stopped at the door and waved me in. "There are women servants inside who will wait upon you," he said as he turned back to his library.

In the great bedchamber Madame Ch'ü lay in state in a marvelously carved wooden bed hung with heavy curtains.

Gorgeous red embroideries formed a canopy above the curtains. I wondered how in the world I could ever examine a patient within such an enclosure.

The maids brought in a heavy blackwood chair and set it down beside the bed. They started to describe their mistress' ailments. Evidently she had coached them herself to explain to the foreign doctor just when her illness had started, which of the animals of the zodiac was in the ascendancy, and what the weather conditions were at the hour when her fever set in.

Having heard their recital, I asked a few further questions of the invisible patient. The whole scene reminded me of those old worshipers who, whenever they consulted an oracle, spoke from behind a veil.

Presently Madame Ch'ü spoke in a somewhat husky voice, supplementing what the maids had said. After I had made a few further inquiries, I was surprised to see the curtains part slightly and the patient's hand come through. In her hand she held a little ivory figure of a reclining woman, completely undressed. "It is not considered seemly," she said, "for a Chinese lady of rank to be examined by a man doctor, so I am handing you this ivory figure marked in two places, the chest and the abdomen, to show you exactly where the pain is located."

I was glad to examine the little ivory piece carefully and hoped I might add it to my Chinese medical collection. After extending the ivory figure to me, Madame Ch'ü kept her right hand through the curtains and I saw at once that she expected me to examine her pulse. After the right wrist, the left hand came out through the curtains. I felt both pulses with care.

A few more questions followed about the fever and sore throat. Then before I could turn to the question of medication, Madame Ch'ü added, "Don't forget to tell me what foods are prohibited." Little by little the wisdom of the old Chinese saying became evident to the doctor:

> Before prescribing medicine,
> Explain to the patient
> What foods to avoid.

The Chinese had no word for "soft diet," but I explained that she could take rice gruel and tea and fruit juices. She was doubtful about the latter. Fruits she thought of as something extraneous to a regular diet, something difficult to classify as *hot* or *cold*. I soon discovered that Madame Ch'ü had read all the writings of the ancient physicians about diet. There was little that I could add.

XV

"EVEN THOUGH HE IS
A FOREIGNER"

醫不三世

不服其藥

The physic of a doctor in whose family medicine has not
Been practised for three generations should not be taken.

Not long after the visit to Mrs. Têng I was awakened one
night during the second watch, just before midnight, by a loud
banging at our front gate. "Please hurry, doctor! Mrs. Ch'êng
is in labor!" I could tell by the repeated knocking and shouting
of the messenger that it was a serious case.

Armed with a black obstetrical bag as well as a long fish
kettle for boiling the instruments, I set out within a few minutes for the Ch'êng home. The servant who brought the
message was to guide me, so there was no danger of my losing
the way. It was midnight now and the downpour that had

continued for two days had turned the streets into racing rivers, hardly navigable for a pedestrian; but I thought I could get past the ward barriers better on foot than in a sedan chair.

Such darkness! Over one doorway a tiny covered lantern sputtered, its wick lying in a saucer partly filled with bean oil; over another, a feeble ray from a tiny kerosene oil lamp, set in a wooden shelter, tried to penetrate the blackness. Even these were there because some family had been unusually philanthropic and had footed the bill for the little beacon outside the great front gate. It would never do to have abundant illumination in this part of the city, for it would merely advertise wealth and lure the night-prowling thief. Actually, the occasional gleams of light, reflected in the rushing torrent that made the whole street its channel, barely let the pedestrian see the dangers of the watery way he was traveling.

Suddenly we ran headlong into a pair of balustrade doors that barred the street completely. They were locked after the second watch.

"I'll wake up the gate watchman, sir."

"But where will you find him? All the houses seem to be locked for the night."

But he told me that this was a district gate, one that separated the wards. Each gate had its own watchman who slept in the tiny cubbyhole overhead. This one, he said, was the hardest to waken of the three watchmen he had passed on the way to my house.

The man's shouts were loud enough to waken everybody on the street, but there was no response from the hole above the barred gate. I looked up at the space; it couldn't have been longer than a full-grown man and surely not over two feet high and two feet wide. To sleep in that bit of a hole would be like sleeping in a coffin.

My guide was still shouting.

"What do you want?" a gruff voice called.

"Come on down and unlock the gate!"

"Huh! Not now! Come back after daybreak!"

"No! Come at once, the foreign doctor is going to attend a woman in childbirth. She is having a difficult time. Hurry down, you old rascal, or I'll report you to the magistrate to-morrow."

"Why doesn't the woman get a midwife? Why does she send for a doctor in the middle of the night? A man doctor, too! Receiving babies is not a man's business!"

"Stop your grumbling, old fellow. You can't stay there till spring, all wrapped up like a bear. Come down, and hurry."

"I'm coming, I'm coming. But it's terribly cold down there. I can see the breath out of your mouths."

Gradually the sleepy form shook itself loose from a dilapidated, cotton-padded comforter. He had wrapped himself in it every night for years—decades probably. We could hear him grumbling. "It's all right for the fire companies or the governor's bodyguard to come through like this after the second watch, but why a doctor? And if he has any prestige, why does he walk through such flooded streets at this hour?"

More unshuffling in the little cubicle up there, and, finally, a thin, ragged form backed slowly down the tiny ladder. Then the gatekeeper groaned that he had forgotten the key. Another climb up to fetch it, another climb down. The long heavy key was fitted into the rusty, iron lock, a ray from our lantern guiding his fingers till he found the keyhole. Finally, squeaking loudly, the barred gate was pushed open.

I kept wondering what was happening to the poor patient.

Splashing on through the darkness, we finally reached a better part of the city where there were more pretentious houses and better lighted doorways. There were two more barriers to be passed with the same slow process before we reached the

Ch'êng home. My attendant banged with the big brass knocker, and a servant within threw open the big doors. "Are you the foreign doctor, sir? The *t'ai-t'ai* is in great distress. Please come this way quickly."

When I reached the bedside of the patient, I found that she had already been in labor forty-eight hours. Obviously she was fairly well worn out. It took but a few minutes to discover that an instrumental delivery would be necessary.

Picture the situation! No nurse, no anesthetist, not a soul who had ever assisted a modern doctor. No electric current, of course; the only light in the room came from two small tin lamps with tiny wicks lighted with kerosene. Fortunately, as in every Chinese house, there was an abundant supply of boiling water on the brick stove in the kitchen.

I had brought along sterile sheets and towels, but how in the world should I be able to get the patient anesthetized? Could I possibly use those elderly women, plainly the midwives, who had been eyeing me suspiciously ever since I came in? Their clothes were filthy and their dingy sleeves reached down to the middle of their palms. I was sure their hands were as unwashed as those of the gatekeepers we had wakened on the way over. They had clearly failed to deliver the baby, and as a result their expressions were a blend of irritation at the foreign doctor who had been called in to supplant them and of apprehension lest they should be unable to collect any fee. No, I must get along without the help of those ignorant women.

Just then I noted a likely looking young servant girl, evidently fresh from the country, standing at the side of the room, waiting for orders. Her large feet (this was before the revolution of 1911 which drove out the Manchu Dynasty and made bound feet unpopular) made me fairly certain that she had been bought by the family as a slave. She looked strong enough for anything, so I took her into an adjoining room, got out the

The Sweetmeat Vendor Blowing Animals from Sugar Paste

No Vitamin Deficiency in Hunan

The Peddler of Chinaware

Little Basket Boy

chloroform bottle, and showed her how to drop the fluid, one drop at a time, on the mask.

"*Ih, êr, san, sz*—One, two, three, four. Just so fast. Drop one drop each time I count. No faster. Now, can you do it exactly as I showed you?"

"I'll try, sir. You must count very distinctly, for the *t'ai-t'ai* is sure to be groaning. I never did it before, sir!"

There was no special bed available—nothing but a low, wide cot, uncomfortable at best, with nothing but a padded quilt laid on crossed fiber ropes. I knew it had been dreadfully tiring for the poor body that had lain there two whole days in intense pain.

The men of the family withdrew, one by one, without a word. Childbirth was something they always left entirely to the women relatives. I asked the husband, just before he left the room, why all the cupboards and drawers were standing wide open; even the trunks in the bedroom and adjoining rooms had their covers up, open as wide as could be.

"It has always been our custom in China to open every possible door and drawer and to throw up every trunk lid at the time a child is being born. The women believe it helps to make certain that the birth canal will stay wide open."

"But don't the midwives have any drug that will relieve pain? And don't they ever wash up? See how dirty their hands are."

"Well, we men leave all that to the womenfolk of the family," he reminded me. "I have never heard them instruct the midwives to clean up. That would be something to insist on, wouldn't it? We must try to get a bit more modern science into the womenfolk of our families." He started toward the door. "You were very good to trouble to come over in the middle of the night."

Ih, êr, san, sz, I counted and, as I counted, I heard the maidservant repeating softly *ih, êr, san, sz,* while she dropped the chloroform on the mask.

I had never seen a group anywhere so evidently full of fear. The shadows on the taut and wrinkled features of those watching women made each of them look as if she were wearing a tragic mask in some demon play. They huddled in the corner of the room as the deep rhythmic breathing of the patient showed that she was becoming unconscious.

When anesthesia was deep enough, I went ahead, fearful all the while lest my newly trained chloroformist faint or collapse with nervousness. She was under a dreadful strain and told me afterward that she trembled as she realized what the family might do to her if the inhaling of the powerful drug caused the patient to stop breathing.

But she did her job well; she was careful and steady while I worked with the instruments. Before long, the hoped-for son arrived. His vigorous cries roused the women in the room from their crouching and fear, and the dark room, lighted only by those two kerosene lamps, became a scene of rejoicing. They sent for the father as soon as the boy was dressed in his bright red garments. Presently we were all congratulating each other.

Kung hsi! Kung hsi!—Congratulations. The father's wish has been granted. He has a piece of jade!

The man came up to me beaming and grateful. "We shall name the boy for you."

Again the doors swung open to let me out into the alley; again we made our way through the darkness, rousing the keeper of the first ward barrier. Dawn broke before we passed the second and third and saw the towsled, drowsy watchmen coming down from their roosting places to vanish into some obscure corner of the city until another night should fall.

It was four o'clock when I got home, and I was glad to snatch a few hours of sleep before the day's work began again at the busy Yali Hospital. Before noon the word was passed around from house to house along South Gate Main Street that a man doctor might be looked to for almost a miracle when childbirth was delayed, "even though he is a foreigner."

XVI

THE GREAT PEACE DOOR

玉不琢不
成器人不
磨不成道

Only with cutting is jade shaped to use;
Only through adversity does man achieve the Way.

FROM my contact with all types of patients at the hospital I soon became aware that China was seething with the restlessness of impending political change. In the cities from Peking to Canton there were tension and bitterness between partisans of the old and new orders. At the beginning of 1910 the Manchu authorities, supported by the conservative landed gentry, tried, once again, as their day of power drew to its close, to turn the enmity of the people away from themselves and against all Westerners.

In Changsha the situation suddenly became tense. The price of rice was soaring. People on the streets, unable to buy even minimal supplies, stormed the magistrate's yamen, shouting that the officials were to blame. One of the gentry, old irreconcilable Yeh Ma-tsŭ, seized the chance. Working with some of his cronies, he roused the mob and inflamed it to action against the foreigners. At the hospital, we were watching—not greatly alarmed but wondering what would happen.

At one o'clock on the morning of April 14, a rude knock on our bedroom door roused us. There stood the gatekeeper, his eyes as big as saucers.

"I *Shêng*, I *Shêng!*—Doctor, doctor!"

"What's the trouble?" I called back, awake in an instant.

"You must run immediately." He shouted that mobs of rioters were rushing through the streets and had set fire to the Norwegian Mission a few doors away. They had also smashed the China Inland Mission in the Street of the Court of Education. We were between the two. The gatekeeper had barred the inner doors but the mob might force the gates.

"Tell T'ang Sz-fu to get sedan chairs for the ladies," I called. "They will take the children on their laps. The men can walk."

"No, sir! No, sir! That will never do! You cannot go out on the street, but you must escape at once!"

Escape at once but without going out on the street? We had no underground corridors. Then the solution flashed into our minds. We would go through the *T'ai P'ing Mên*—the Gate of Great Peace. This was a secret doorway, always kept plastered up with mud and whitewashed like the rest of the wall at the back of the compound. Every Chinese residence had such a potential doorway at the back, as far as possible from the front gate. It was as if Chinese families built their houses on the assumption that attack might come at any time, from fire or flood or rioters, and that the neighbor whose house adjoined at the back would always provide safe refuge. The one familiar way of escape from danger was through this "door of peace," never through the front gate or by leaping across the firewall from one rooftop to another.

We told the gateman we would go out through that door. He nodded approval and ran downstairs to assemble the other servants.

The "compound" consisted of our family with three little children, aged six, four, and one, with three other American adults and another baby. There was no time for a conference. I called instructions from our courtyard to get food ready and to take money along. My wife put several cans of condensed milk and a thermos bottle of boiled water into the picnic basket and picked up a few warm clothes for the youngsters. Fortunately, it was the fourteenth of April and spring weather was well advanced. For my part, I took from the strongbox in my study my whole supply of available cash—fifty silver dollars, together with a good supply of the red calling cards, eight inches by four, that everyone used in those days before the revolution. No choice could have been wiser, as events proved.

The houseboy, Yüan Sz-fu, brought me a hatchet from the kitchen, and a couple of strokes opened the way through the door of peace. We scarcely realized, when we broke through at half-past one that morning, what friendly and hospitable persons Chinese neighbors could be. We knew nothing whatever about them. We had never exchanged calls. Their front gate and ours opened on parallel streets, two hundred yards apart; they were actually in different wards of the city. And yet that midnight intrusion of foreigners was received with a welcome.

We discovered, later, that they knew the American doctor was just over the wall. Friends who lived next door to them on the north had called me in consultation some months previously when a young mother there had nearly died in labor. Her recovery and the well-being of the child had made householders throughout that part of the city speak appreciatively of Western obstetrics. Yet they always added, when they spoke of the doctor, "Why does a man doctor accept midnight calls to attend a woman in childbirth? He should know that is a midwife's job!"

The whole family turned out to meet us. They saw us carrying the little children and rushed to their bedrooms to snatch their own children from their beds. They urged us to dress our children in the little Chinese padded garments their children wore in winter. "Be quick!" they urged. "The rioters may rush right through the length of your house, plunge through the peace door and find you all here in our corridor. Put your children into these clothes quickly, and let them lie in these beds. We'll cover them up with heavy comforters, and no rioter will ever know that they are Westerners. You grown-up guests should put on these heavy robes and sit quietly in the room where the children are going to sleep. We'll keep guard for you."

It would have been hard to imagine American neighbors so hospitable to people of another race in the middle of the night, when fires were raging in near-by streets. They might well have thought it dangerous to give us shelter. They had probably heard what an antiforeign turn the affair was taking, and had no way of knowing whether the governor could keep the situation in hand. Yet when we entered their home, they acted as if it were all quite according to tradition.

We got the children into bed and turned the kerosene lights low. Even though our children were thrilled at the midnight drama, it was not going to be easy to sit there waiting for the morning.

I sent for T'ang, the cook, and handed him five urgent messages that I had written on the long red calling cards. I told him he must arrange to have them all delivered promptly. One was to go to the captain of the British steamer, asking him not to sail for Hankow at the usual early-morning hour but to wait until our safety was assured; two to my school and hospital colleagues; one to the British consul (we had no American consul in Changsha till 1915); and one to General Yang who commanded all the imperial battalions stationed outside the Liuyang Gate.

I knew the messages would get through, for the cook was a native son. One silver dollar—a lot of money in those days— was to be paid each messenger who brought me a reply. We sat and waited, anxious and wondering. There was no way of knowing whether the Chinese in Changsha were going to turn against *us*.

In about an hour T'ang brought in the first of the replies. Captain Agassiz promised not to sail until he heard from us. Some of our friends in the other missions of the city sent us word. Practically all their properties suffered, some smashed to bits by vandals, others completely gutted.

Just at daybreak, we heard the sound of soldiers marching. Our host came and told us that General Yang had sent a hundred men with rifles and fixed bayonets to escort us out to the camp east of the city. They were waiting for us in the street outside. Before we started, our hospitable friends served us hot tea and helped the women and children into the sedan chairs that had been brought in for them. The men walked along beside the chairs through the quiet streets, usually so crowded at this hour of the early-morning market. Now they were utterly vacant. Even the police sentry boxes along the main streets were empty, having been knocked over by the mob. Presently we reached the Liuyang Gate and found that the general had given orders to let us through without delay.

Immediately outside the gate we crossed the military road and saw the barracks for which we were headed. A bugle sounded

and our cavalcade of three sedan chairs, following behind a
hundred foot soldiers, entered the enclosure of the barracks.
At headquarters the general himself ran down the steps, greeting us with a military salute. He invited us to rest for a little
while, ordered tea served in our rooms, and asked us to join
him for seven o'clock breakfast.

What a meal it was! General Yang must have feared we
might go hungry for several days and told his cook to feed
us generously.

After breakfast the sedan chairs were ordered again and
we went off through several miles of countryside. The fields
were gay with spring colors, the green of late winter wheat and
the bright yellow of mustard. Here and there were patches of
tender bamboo. Every farmhouse seemed to be set in a garden
of great tree peonies. In the distance, across the river, Yolu
Shan was ablaze with the pink and red of azaleas. Turning
along the north wall, we swung round down to the river and
soon reached the British consulate.

Early in the afternoon the consul secured a launch for us
and sent our party upstream to where Captain Agassiz had anchored in the middle of the river. Our hearts sank to see big
puffs of smoke and then flames break out in one part of the
city after another. As soon as we got aboard the S.S. *Siangtan*,
we crowded the decks on the city side and watched with dis-
may that terrible sight. The city in which we had lived and
worked for years seemed to be going up in flames. We could
count at least thirty fires. There on the foreshore we could
see the ruins of the Imperial Customs House and near it the
charred remains of the warehouses belonging to the two British steamship companies. Every time a new fire broke out we
tried to guess whose property it was.

As one group of our friends after another made its way from
the shore in little sampans and reached the steamer, the ship

began to look like a refugee camp. Gradually the stories of the refugees unfolded as we sat round the captain in the dining saloon.

A little before midnight the governor's yamen had been broken into and completely gutted. Then the rioters had rushed down to the Customs House and set that afire. Captain Agassiz told us at dark that his lookouts had counted forty-eight fires that day.

The British consul was the most disconsolate of us all. "Of course," he said, "this means that Westerners will never enter the city again."

That afternoon forty refugees left Changsha for Hankow on a British steamer. The women and children had the inside cabins. For the men there were blankets, and they lay on deck in rows. Halfway to Hankow, we saluted the American gunboat *Villalobos*, hurrying to Changsha to share in patrol duty.

Three days later the men were back in Changsha, carrying on their work as usual. Dr. Hou had a thrilling story about the strength of the friendships which that night had made evident.

We found that the authorities had ordered all the houses of the Yali School and Hospital staff sealed and guarded by government soldiers. Not a door had been forced, not a window-pane broken in our houses or in hospital or school. Our clothes and trinkets were just where we left them when we hurried away that night. Clearly, we were not on the black list of the officials.

Down in West Archway Street the senior gatekeeper of the Yali Preparatory School had concealed the traces of "foreign" occupation there by filling in with mud the plainly cut characters, YALI SCHOOL, on the boundary stones. No casual passer-by would stop to dig them out and reveal the name hidden there.

The most dramatic experience of all had occurred in front of the hospital. A crowd of rioters surged up the street looking for government or "foreign" property to wreck. As they reached the balustrade in front of the Yali Court of Medicine, some of the ruffians shouted, "This is a foreign building! Let's go in and smash it up!"

The mob stopped suddenly and swayed toward the doorway to burst it open, when a broad-shouldered fellow, towering above the crowd, yelled, "Stop! This is the hospital where they took a bullet out of my leg two years ago. If this disturbance goes on, there's sure to be shooting, and some of us are likely to get bullets in our legs. We must leave the hospital for an emergency. We might need it. Move on!"

He spoke with such authority that the mob obeyed and pushed on up the street. The man who had saved the hospital was our first operative patient—Huang, the bandit!

After we had looked through the hospital, delighted that no harm of any sort had been done, Dr. Hou took me into the office. "It was a remarkable experience, that night," he said. "I thought it was all over with us. Of course I was in no danger, being a Chinese like the rest of the people on the street. I just walked away from my room and stayed outside. But look at this." He unfolded a square sheet of coarse yellow paper, about two feet each way—a poster that he had found on the front of the hospital on the day of the riot. On it in large Chinese characters were written these lines:

The Yali Hospital
Is indeed a rented building.
Seeing this time of crisis,
It has moved out and left the building empty.
The street neighborhood guilds have closed and sealed it
To guard against unforeseen danger.
To carry on until the price of rice is normal,

> To save the desolate and care for the indigent,
> Raise a fund of a hundred thousand.
> Let everyone contribute gladly.
> This proclamation is official.
> There is positively no prevarication!
>
> Jointly signed by the Street Guilds
> of Medicine King Street and
> West Archway Street.

That square of yellow paper remains one of our priceless treasures.

XVII

"THE TIME IS NOT YET RIPE"

惟要有心人　天下無難事

Under heaven nothing is difficult to achieve;
All that is needed is a man with a heart.

IN HANKOW, where I was attending the biennial China Medical Missions Conference of 1910, I went down to the pier to greet Dr. Yen, the young Chinese physician who had been trained at Yale and was coming out to work with me. To be able to lay down half the load immediately seemed to me something of a miracle.

It was not difficult to recognize Dr. Yen among the passengers crowded at the rail. A slender Chinese youth, not yet thirty, wearing a heavy American overcoat, stepped briskly off the gangplank, a contrast to the other passengers in costume, gait, and alertness. The other Chinese gentlemen were still wearing the queues of the old Manchu regime and were protected from the cold February winds by heavy padded gowns. As he stepped from the gangplank to the bund, Dr. Yen seemed both to belong to the environment and to be different from it.

"Welcome, cousin!" "Welcome, Doctor Yen!" Several of his relatives shouted greetings to him from the bund where they had been standing for hours, waiting for his ship. Kiukiang was a hundred and fifty miles downriver, and telegrams giving the hour of the steamer's departure from that port provided only an approximate guide as to the time of its arrival in Hankow.

After I had greeted Dr. Yen and introduced myself to the gathered family, we walked together to the home of the cousin. There we flung one question after another at him without a pause for breath, asking him about his two years in South Africa and his four in America. I was eager to know what he had seen in the hospitals of Berlin, Vienna, and Paris which he had visited on the way home.

After a cup of tea with his relatives, I dragged Dr. Yen away to the medical gathering. I didn't want him to miss a single hour of the China Medical Missions Conference which had convened earlier in the afternoon. "There will be medical missionaries and community practitioners on hand from all over Central China. I want you to meet them all and to have them meet my new colleague. You don't appreciate," I went on, "what a godsend it is to have you actually here. I've been waiting for you in Changsha five years. Do you realize that there hasn't been a single modern-trained physician there at the hospital for consultation or to take over part of the load?

By the way, I hope you are keen about surgery. I want to turn over all the operative work to you. If you'll carry that and let me stick to medicine, I shall be eternally grateful."

"Surgery is just what I want," he replied, "and I'm keen about eye work. Do you have a lot of it in Changsha?"

"All you can possibly handle!"

As we walked along the bund, it suddenly came over me that there would be no other Chinese physician at the conference. They were all Americans and British and a few other Europeans. They would give my new colleague a hearty welcome.

"Far too much of the hospital work in Central China is being done by Western doctors," I told him. "They haven't tried to associate Chinese medical graduates of high standard with them as they should have done. But of course," I added, "there are very few Chinese doctors available. I rather imagine that some of the crowd at the conference this afternoon will be startled when you walk in. Remember that you are the forerunner of a new day in China. We'll show them what a cooperative staff of Chinese and Americans can do."

As we walked up the steps of the house where the gathering was assembled, I thought how strange it was that a Chinese doctor should be unexpected in the center of a crowded Chinese metropolis. So far as I knew, there was only one other Chinese physician with Western training in the whole of Central China. I hoped Dr. Yen would make many friends that day.

Our British host was graciousness itself—they were having afternoon tea as we arrived—but the aloof attitude of some of the doctors was distressing to me. One of the older men took me aside and asked, "Who is that young Chinese you brought in with you?"

"That's my new colleague, Doctor Yen, who just arrived today from America."

"Do you mean to tell me that your society in America has sent out a Chinese to be your colleague; really to be on an equal basis with American doctors as a member of your hospital staff?"

"Why not? He has exactly the same sort of professional training you and I have had. He is just as ready to give himself to Christian medical service for his people as we are. After all, they are his fellow countrymen."

"You will be sorry. The time is not yet ripe. Why, it is simply unprecedented. Of course we ought to employ Chinese doctors some day. But it is still far too early to be taking them on our staffs as colleagues. We must train and supervise them. Mind you, you'll be sorry for such a premature action."

The very contrary proved true. Dr. Yen's presence was like a lightning rod, averting many a catastrophe. Nothing else could have so completely won Chinese confidence in that conservative old province of Hunan. Once it was known that a competent Chinese, trained abroad, was a part of the inner circle of Yale-in-China, our medical stock rose in the community and our welcome to the homes and institutions of Changsha became a continuing reality.

Two days later the Hankow medical conference adjourned and we started for Changsha; but when we reached Yochow, the water in the Hsiang River was too low for our steamer to go beyond that halfway point. I told Dr. Yen about my first view of Yochow, five years earlier, and about the blocked archway across the main road that seemed at the time like a premonition of opposition in Hunan province.

The next morning we hired a long, narrow sailing boat to carry us the rest of the way, and did the hundred miles to Changsha in seventeen hours, with a strong following wind all the way. The good spirits must have heeded the big character *Shun*—Favoring—painted in gold high up on the stern.

That night, as the boat sailed along, the only external sounds were the grunting of twenty-four pigs below deck and the rush of the water as we cut through it. Inside the little deck cabin, as we huddled together to keep warm, I begged Dr. Yen to tell me about his home and his earlier years.

His home was in Shanghai but his family had come originally from Fukien province from which they had escaped when the Taiping Rebels devastated the land. When his grandparents reached Shanghai they were given shelter by a Chinese pastor. The two sons entered the school that later became St. John's University. When he graduated, the older brother was sent to America to take a theological course, and on his return to China he became eminent among the leaders of the Episcopal church. The younger brother, too, went to America and entered Kenyon College. This was at the height of the American Civil War. When the entire student body of Kenyon College went off to fight in the Union Army, young Yen was among them. After the war was over, he came back to college, finished his studies, was ordained as an Episcopal priest, and sent to a parish in one of the northern suburbs of Shanghai. There he met in an adjoining parish another young priest named Wu, who also had recently returned from America. He, too, had fought in the Union Army during the last year of the American Civil War. Soon Yen, the young clergyman, married his colleague's sister. Dr. Yen was their second son.

"What an inheritance you have!" I exclaimed. "Yours is a story of two continents."

After graduating from preparatory school in Shanghai, Dr. Yen had taken science courses for a couple of years and then entered St. John's Medical School. He was part way through when a call came for medical assistants to work among the Chinese laborers in the diamond mines of South Africa. He was all for the adventure, but after reaching Africa he realized that his training had not been sufficiently basic, especially in chemistry, anatomy, and physiology. Meanwhile, his Chinese friends in America were urging him to come there and take a full medical course, so he finally pulled out of Africa and went to New Haven.

He hadn't foreseen how much harder the medical course at Yale was going to be. The medical vocabularies were terribly difficult, and he could scarcely endure the cold weather. Then, too, his family in Shanghai couldn't understand why, since he had a scholarship, he should be writing home for more money every little while.

"Couldn't you make it clear that a medical course was the most expensive of all professional courses?" I asked.

"Yes, they understood after the first year," he said. "But that first year I worked so hard that my own strength gave out."

By Thanksgiving Yen was so thoroughly discouraged that he decided to throw it all up and return to China. The fact of having reached a decision seemed like a tonic, and on Thanksgiving night, he walked up and down Chapel Street, looking without much concern into the shop windows, glad that he would soon be back home in China. Suddenly he heard the voice of A. C. Williams, an old American friend. "You're just the man I'm looking for," Williams called out. "I'm sorry I didn't have you up in Hartford today for our family Thanksgiving dinner. We talked about you there and I rushed down to New Haven to make a proposal to you. I want you, after you become a doctor, to go out to work with Ed Hume in Changsha."

Yen told him it was impossible. He had made up his mind to sail for Shanghai the following week.

But his American friend was not to be denied. He linked his arm in Yen's; then they stopped for a cup of hot coffee and talked about Changsha far into the night. The next day Yen didn't buy the ticket to Shanghai. Before long the Yale-in-

China executive committee accepted him and he agreed, if his family in Shanghai were willing, to offer definitely for Chang-sha.

"Did you ever weaken about finishing the medical course?" I inquired.

"No! And I was lucky enough to get one of the graduation prizes, which seemed to cheer the family, who were scolding me for staying so long in America. Last summer, I went over to England to get a diploma in tropical medicine, and now here I am, ready to work."

The boat raced along with a following north wind that blew stronger all the way. We were wrapped in extra comforters against the cold of that blustery February night. The next day the sun was shining brightly when our boat made fast outside the Little West Gate. As we walked through the narrow streets together, I realized that on this day a new era in modern medicine was opening in Changsha. From now on there would be two of us, a Chinese doctor and an American doctor, working together. It was an old Chinese philosopher who said: "If two men are of one mind, their keenness will cut metal!"

XVIII
CULTURAL TRADITIONS

習 性
相 相
遠 近

By nature men are nearly alike;
Their customs differ widely.

IT WAS years before we discovered what lay behind many of
the reactions we met in Changsha. Westerners often said to
me, casually, "Surely you don't find Chinese patients as sensi-
tive to pain, as emotionally responsive, as Westerners are."
Such an assumption always seemed to me superficial.

I began to find out, as time went on, what the crises were
that left a patient unmoved and in what situations he would
burst into a fit of anger or become violently obstinate. Gradually I learned that events in the day's experience that lay within
the bounds of familiar tradition, and that kept him related to
the cosmos as he understood it, caused no disturbance of his
equanimity.

The death of a criminal, for instance, no matter how gruesome, was to be expected. The execution of a patient of mine,

I remember, roused no resentment in the others, although it had a disturbing effect upon me. The man whom I had treated in the hospital was charged with being a member of a disreputable organization and was sentenced to death. I was not competent to judge as to whether or not he had received a fair trial. When he was led out along West Long Street to the execution ground, his hands and feet heavy with clanking chains, I followed the group. As I walked behind the prisoner and his guards, I glanced up and saw, suspended in wooden cages on posts at several street intersections, the heads of prisoners who had been executed the day before at the governor's order.

There was an air of solemnity along the whole length of the street. People averted their eyes, both from the prisoner as he walked along and from the exposed heads. But there was no sense of rebellion against authority, nor did the imposing of the extreme penalty break into the cycle of the familiar. The Chinese attitude toward the ordered universe has always been to consider danger, disease, disaster, and death as a normal part of the universe, like health and happiness.

> To accept this and live accordingly is wisdom;
> To struggle impatiently,
> To chafe and strike out in resistance
> Is simply to misunderstand
> The nature of the cosmic process.

Neither did catastrophes of nature disturb them. Early one morning we were awakened by a terrific clap of thunder and, soon after, a messenger rushed to the house to summon me to see an injured man at the North Gate. When I got there the patient was dead. He had been killed by lightning, and the burned body was a gruesome sight. Even I, a doctor, was upset.

"How terrible!" I remarked to the crowd that had gathered.

"Oh, no, sir," one man insisted. "It was as it should be. That man was the meanest fellow in Changsha. Today, before daylight, this wretched thief crept up in the darkness and snatched the string of cash that was tied around the neck of a baby lying in a basket in front of the Home for Foundlings."

"He tried to get away," another speaker burst in, "but he hadn't gone more than fifty feet before the gods got him. The God of Thunder is always on the watch to discover and execute wicked people. He is accompanied by a goddess who uses a mirror to flash a blinding light on the victim."

"Quick work by the goddess!" I said to the bystanders.

"Oh, sir, the thief ought to be punished promptly. The gods see to that."

On another occasion I was permitted by the governor to attend the execution of three notorious criminals, two men and a woman. The execution ground was not far from the yamen, and I was told to be on hand in the morning not later than six o'clock. Soldiers were drawn up at both ends of the arena and the block was in the center. Priests in their temple robes were present to grant absolution, not only to the criminals, but also to the executioner whose own status would need clearing in the spirit world.

When the time arrived, the executioner handed his sword to an assistant and went over to where the three criminals were standing, manacled. He knelt down before each of the three and kotowed as one might who was venerating his ancestors. This cleared him of offence, for he made the profound apology that Chinese recognize. And the prisoners, too, had saved face. They had received the obeisance of the kotow.

Before they were led to the block, I asked the governor's secretary, my official guide, whether I might, as a doctor, count the pulse of each prisoner. He gave permission and went with me to them. One of the men had a pulse count of 72, the other of 74. The woman's pulse was 78. My own pulse was 128!

Suicide, like death, was no unfamiliar event in China. A wife might try to kill herself in revenge for her husband's cruelty. A disgraced official might hope, by ending his own life, to bring his superior into disfavor. Many thought that they might save face by cutting their own throats.

A cook in a Chinese home near by told his young apprentice of a suicide that had just occurred next door, and added, "Do you realize, you poor, useless thing, what a relief it would be to your wife, out in the home village, as well as to us all, if you, too, were to end your life?"

The youth lost face completely, for this rebuke had been uttered in the presence of the other servants. So he went out, took an overdose of opium, and lay down to die at the door of the cook's room. Now his *shên*, his ethereal spirit, would hover round and haunt the cook in continuing revenge. No coroner's inquest was needed, nor any legal trial: the officials to whom the case was reported were familiar enough with this method of seeking vengeance. But the servants begged us to keep all our house lights burning that night. The dead man's spirit might prowl round in the dark, and even venture within our walls.

Wives who wished to spite their husbands usually tried one or the other of two methods of suicide. One was to snatch a gold ring off the finger and swallow it. Many a time a young wife was brought hurriedly into the dispensary. "Doctor, doctor!" the relatives would plead. "Help her, quick! She has swallowed gold. Act quickly or it will be the death of her!"

Where the belief started that to swallow a gold ring would be fatal, I cannot say. If death ever occurred under such cir-

cumstances, it may have been because an overdose of opium
was swallowed at the same time.

The surer method for the wife, if she planned death in
earnest, was to jump into a well in the family courtyard. Wells
in Changsha were kept covered with a heavy slab of granite,
and the opening in the slab was just big enough to admit the
family bucket. It would take so long to uncover the well that
the poor wife would almost always have a running start toward
the carrying out of her purpose. If she died, the poor husband
lost face in the community. Little chance that another mate
would soon trust herself to him.

One could always ward off avenging spirits after a suicide
by hanging a charm at the head of the bed. Best of all charms
were the swords made of old brass or copper cash strung together. To make the charm effective, the sword must be kept
in the room where the suicide had occurred. Then the emperors whose reigns the coins commemorated would grant protection from hovering spirits. Thereafter the spirits would serve
as guardians of the living. Death, suicide, these were accepted
by Chinese tradition and so did not stir the emotions unduly.

In the hospital, we found that as long as our treatment followed directions that they understood, our patients exhibited
no fear. Thus, to my surprise, when I suggested operating on
an elderly man's eyes for double cataract, the relatives seemed
entirely willing. "We had expected to take him," they said,
"to the famous eye doctor, Fang, near the northwest gate. He
has been *needling* eyes for more than a generation."

The cataract operation could be done without general
anesthetic and the friends of the patient were reassured when
I promised them that the patient would feel no pain. Cataract
cases became quite a fad in Changsha. People knew they had
to be treated with instruments.

It always increased the patient's confidence if he saw me

write out a prescription. This was particularly true in the private homes of the conservative gentry. *"Ch'ing hsien shêng k'ai fang*—Please, doctor, 'open a prescription' "—was the invariable request after the diagnosis was made.

Gradually I learned a great deal about the wealth of herbs used as medicaments in China. Apparently all the drugs in the native pharmacopoeia were indigenous save two, alfalfa and the grape. These had been imported from Iran over two thousand years earlier and had been used for both fodder and medication. Everyone thought of them that way. The amazing thing was not that so many vegetable remedies were native to China (*ma huang,* for example, from which ephedrine is derived) but that so many animal products were also recognized as potent for treatment.

Decades earlier, Sir Patrick Manson, when he was practising in Amoy, treated a Western woman for pernicious anemia without success. She was treated later by an eminent Chinese doctor of the old school, who promised to cure her. He fed her large doses of crow's liver, and she made surprising progress, much to the surprise of Manson. This was scores of years before Western science discovered liver as a specific remedy for that disease.

In some cases, the treatment we proposed was cheerfully accepted without its being realized that for centuries the Chinese' own doctors had been using the same substance in another form. Thus, seaweed extracts (which we know contain iodine) were regularly prescribed for certain kinds of goiter, and the livers of certain fat fish for tuberculous conditions. Empirical and experimental medicine were becoming remarkably near neighbors.

Vaccination, moreover, was readily accepted by everyone. A Buddhist nun, in the reign of the Emperor Jen Tsung, climbed to the summit of Mount Omei in Szechwan, near the Tibetan border, and taught inoculation against smallpox. True, modern lymph was prepared from the calf, but this was essentially the same method of preventing smallpox. No procedure in modern preventive medicine was more widely trusted. At first we had to send to the coastal cities for supplies of vaccine, but as soon as the National Health Administration got under way, its earliest programs included the manufacture of vaccines and serums. Our dispensary was for a long time the chief center of vaccination in Changsha.

However, once we proposed anything outside the familiar round, obstacles sprang up. No one had ever heard of administering chloroform or ether. "What!" a mother shouted at me once. "You are going to put that big white thing over my boy's nose and mouth? Never! He wouldn't be able to breathe. That would be worse than the executioner. He does everything out in the open."

Many a time I mourned at losing the chance to treat a patient surgically. At first people were simply not conditioned to accept any such serious adventure into the unknown. But after a time, I began to suggest that I would put the patient to sleep with *mêng yao*, dream medicine. Sleep was known and dreams were familiar enough. To guarantee that a cutting operation could be done without pain opened, little by little, the doors of surgical opportunity.

But there were two regions, naturally enough, where surgical intervention was absolutely refused for many years. If we proposed operations on the trunk or skull, "Never!" they would say. "We'll risk his death from disease rather than let you cut into his head."

They told me that even the most famous surgeon of Chinese history, Hua T'o, of the period of the Three Kingdoms, had lost his life because he dared to suggest trephining the skull of an illustrious general. Hua T'o's proposal was just as sound in A.D. 220 as were the proposals of the American doctor seventeen hundred years later. But the authority of the great chieftain to forbid was no greater than that of the mother in Changsha who feared for the life of her husband or daughter. To suggest that tension within the skull called for surgical intervention was something so extraordinary, so far from the familiar cultural tradition, that it was always met with a veto.

Underneath all these traditions lay deep religious roots. The ordinary man on the street was concerned to keep himself and his family within the stream of life as he understood it. His concepts of disease and health were profoundly influenced by the teachings of both Taoism and Buddhism.

I learned this once in a picturesque way when a grateful patient, one of the leaders of the Changsha gentry, sent me a gift of a pair of scrolls, mounted on heavy silk. The scrolls carried paired inscriptions suggesting that the "foreign doctor," too, had come under the ancient spell. On one scroll were included the words, *Fang Hu*, and on the other, *P'u T'i Shu*.

Fang Hu, the Square Kettle (so called because it was shaped like a teakettle), was one of the three Islands of the Blest. In an old legend it was said to be inhabited by fairies, who "do not eat the five grains, who inhale air and drink dew. The vegetation there is miraculous, the flowers are sweet scented. If the fruits of these islands are eaten, they will preserve the eater from old age and death." It was a graceful tribute to a doctor to think of him as having been taken in spirit to those sacred islands of Taoism, there to be taught the art of prolonging life. Many dispensaries and apothecaries' shops all over

China still carry the name of the Square Kettle as a symbol of immortality.

P'u T'i Shu, the Tree of Knowledge, linked me with Buddhism and its healing influence. Everyone knew that Buddha had sat for years under the bodhi tree and attained perfect knowledge there. Well might a teacher of medicine gain by wandering in such groves of wisdom!

Far older, however, than Taoism and Buddhism was the practice of ancestor worship, which has been unquestionably the most potent of all the forces that have held the Chinese people to traditional ways. The ancient Chinese were eager that the spirits of their ancestors should understand the needs and difficulties of their descendants in health and disease as well as in other matters. To obtain the counsel of these powerful spirits they wrote to them on inflammable material and burned it. The smoke carried up to heaven the message they sought to send. This desire to communicate with the spirits was a powerful incentive to the development of the written language.

The Chinese believe that, whatever the source of one's religious belief, life is one throughout the universe. Man's soul, to attain immortality, must develop in harmony with all life. He must find health, not only through the processes of physical and chemical biology, but by bringing both spirit and body into adjustment with the forces of the universe.

Life-conferring qualities were found in gold and jade and pearls because of some mystic relation that they were believed to have with heaven. Wise men used these powers both to prolong life and to prevent decomposition after death. Every now and then an ancient tomb, dating back to the Chou Dynasty, was excavated near Changsha and yielded superb pieces of jade, round and beautifully carved. These had been placed in the mouths of the deceased or used to close other orifices. Back in the fourth century Ko Hung exclaimed: "Gold, jade, and pearls are the *tsing* [essence] of Heaven and Earth; he who consumes them shall live as long as Heaven and Earth."

XIX

"HE KEPT PLAGUE AWAY"

故聖人不
治已病治
未病

The ancient sages did not treat those who were already ill;
They instructed those who were not ill.

Dr. Yen had come to the hospital none too soon. Even with his help we could not fully meet our opportunities. The Manchu Dynasty was cracking up; we had realized it dimly in 1908 when both Emperor Kwang Hsu and the Empress Dowager died in the same week and our hospital walls were adorned for a month with white mourning scrolls. We had realized it vividly during the April riots of 1910.

By the beginning of 1911, it was common knowledge that a serious political overturn was at hand. Our sedan chair bearers told us, as we made our round of official New Year's calls, that more executions had been ordered during the last weeks of the old year than for a score of years. Every time I made a medical call at any official's yamen, the chair bearers picked up news about the severe measures now ordered to crush rebellion. It wouldn't be long now, even the hospital coolies told me, before the explosion. The revolutionary planners were, of course, working under the direction of Dr. Sun Yat-sen. Everywhere men rallied to his leadership, though they knew that the Manchu court had spies watching for him everywhere.

At the hospital we had an excellent opportunity to learn how young China was responding. A serious epidemic broke out in one of the leading government schools in Changsha, and the principal, a good friend of ours, urged the parents to send their boys to us for treatment. Scarcely had I started to examine them when they burst out with their grievances. Their teachers were angry because the governor had not organized a health department. The name of their school was Light of China Middle School, and they used modern textbooks, but their government had done nothing about civic health. In America, they had read, every pupil had to be vaccinated and to undergo a yearly health examination. The teachers said the Manchu Dynasty was to blame for China's lack of progress and ought to be thrown out at once. They quoted an ancient saying: "It is more dangerous to stop the mouth of the people than to dam the mouth of the river."

Pupils from the famous Chou Nan girls' school appeared at the dispensary with bobbed hair—something unheard of in the old decorous regime—and they often came in twos and threes, unescorted. The aristocratic ladies of old China thought it most unseemly for girls to be unchaperoned on the street, but the parents appeared powerless to stop it. "Of course we came by ourselves," girls would say. "We know this is a good hospital, we know our way through the streets, so why not? Besides, we shall have a new government in Peking before long."

Most vivid of all the warnings were the anti-Manchu rallies held in the main auditorium of the Hunan Educational Association. The building itself was a sign of the new day, for it was erected on the site of the old provincial examination halls where, for centuries, scholars had come to sit for grueling classical tests. One little block of the cubicles was still standing, a sort of museum piece to remind citizens of their ancient customs.

It was like a breath of fresh air to go over to the gatherings at the association and to see the great open space cleared in front, "for athletic contests." We foresaw that Hunan could not continue to live any longer in the age in which the Yali School came into being, when one of the pupils was asked, "What do you do for exercise?" and replied, "I eat with my chopsticks!"

Once in a while a group of friends, including many of the gentry, would ask whether they could have a private meeting in our dispensary waiting room. "We won't come," they said, "till you are through your morning's medical consultations." As I passed the door of the room one afternoon, I heard a man saying, his voice raised unusually high, "Yes, we all know that the Manchu emperors were patrons of art and literature. And Europeans got to know them because they employed eminent Western scientists to correct the calendar and to acquaint China with new kinds of learning."

"Yes, yes," interrupted another speaker, greatly agitated, "but they never turned a hand to improve the health of the nation. Every other country has health departments in all its great cities. What have we here in Changsha?"

The awakening of this interest in public health rewarded our medical men for years of laboratory study devoted to finding means for combating the plagues that scourged China. I remember well the excitement in our own laboratory the day

Respectfully Have Pity on Printed
Paper

Pigs on West Archway Street

One of the Nursing
Pioneers

Dr. Wang, My Medical
Consultant

young Ts'ao, our assistant, found something new under the microscope. All the common ova found in dispensary cases he had learned to recognize at a glance, hookworm and round-worm eggs. Each slide had to be checked, of course. Malarial parasites were far beyond his powers. This time he was an-noyed at himself. "This ovum," he insisted, "is different from all the others in size and outline."

It was indeed an unusual slide. The patient was from Siang-yin, forty miles downriver, a place that, we now knew, had some sort of mysterious disease. Many of the cases from there came with swollen abdomens, fever, and other signs of parasitic in-fection. Several of the strange ova were present in the slide that Ts'ao had prepared. The next day another patient came in from Siangyin and he, too, showed the same ova. A differ-ential count of the white blood cells showed, in both cases, six or seven times as many eosinophiles present as in a normal patient. Clearly, some serious parasitic infection was pres-ent.

Then we heard of other cases. Houghton had found them at Wuhu, and Logan had seen them at Changteh, the rice-bowl city west of Tungting Lake. Soon it became clear that this strange infection was widely prevalent throughout the Yangtze Valley. Some called it Kiukiang fever, others, Ichang fever. The *China Medical Journal* began to print reports of cases observed. In the summer of 1910, an American lad up at Yochow, a hundred miles to the north, was found heavily in-fested. His was the first case reported of infection in an Ameri-can.

Meanwhile the *British Journal of Tropical Medicine* showed pictures of the ova, and called the parasite *Schistosoma japoni-cum*. Evidently the disease, about which none of us had ever heard in 1905, had a widespread distribution. We searched each issue of our medical journals for reports of maladies hitherto unknown and for new suggestions as to laboratory procedure. We were clearly at a post on the frontier.

We were surrounded also by typhoid, cholera, and other intestinal diseases spread by the human night soil used as fertilizer. Then, too, there were the more familiar diseases: tuberculosis, smallpox, measles, and many others.

We felt sure tuberculosis of the lungs couldn't have been present in China very long, for people showed little or no resistance, once they fell ill. Students in preparatory schools, young teachers, professional workers of many sorts, developed "galloping consumption" very easily. Some of our most promising young Chinese friends died after the briefest illness. Of course personal and community hygiene were unknown words. Spitting was a habit universally indulged in, within the home and on the street. We hesitated to accept invitations to the homes of friends who, we knew, were infected. How could we possibly dip our chopsticks in the common bowls, however luxurious the feast our host provided?

We began to give more time to vaccination clinics, and lectured in the schools about "fingers, food, flies." The authorities were grateful for every bit of what they called the new science. It was no uncommon experience to have a mother bring a child to the dispensary, covered with smallpox crusts and burning with fever. Often we managed to vaccinate everyone in the clinic who had been exposed, but many were afraid. I wonder how many smallpox epidemics we headed off in that way.

Once, while making night rounds in the maternity ward, I stopped to speak to a woman whose baby was already due. "I am burning with fever, sir," she said, "and have many strange little red lumps on my forehead. I just saw them in the mirror." She had already broken out with smallpox! No use in vaccinating her; but everyone else on the floor was protected immediately. The baby was born safely, and our patient, well isolated, came through unscarred.

Diphtheria, too, was with us often malignant, as well as leprosy and typhus, malaria and all the varieties of pneumonia. It was a remarkable clinical experience and we wondered when we could begin using the material to teach students.

Then in the winter of 1911, pneumonic plague raged in Manchuria. The mortality was 100 per cent. Thousands of lives were lost. Dr. Wu Lien-teh, who had returned from Britain with thorough training in preventive medicine, volunteered to fight the epidemic. Dr. Richard Strong of the American Army joined him, and Dr. Jackson of the Mukden Medical College also volunteered to work with Dr. Wu. After a few weeks of valorous work, Dr. Jackson himself developed the malady in fatal form. In Southeast China another well-known missionary doctor also died of pneumonic plague. Fear of the disease was everywhere. Could it be kept out of Central China?

In the spring the province of Hupeh, just north of us, sent us an urgent request, asking to borrow Dr. Yen. Bubonic plague was coming down the rail line from Peking and energetic measures were needed if it was to be headed off.

We were glad to lend Dr. Yen. Now, surely, was the time to launch out with a new emphasis on public health and community medicine. Dr. Yen talked it over with the city fathers, who knew the mind of the people. He told them about the invitation from Hankow and the doors it would open for public-health campaigns. They insisted that he should go, and reminded him of the traditional Chinese belief:

> The superior doctor prevents sickness;
> The mediocre doctor attends to impending sickness;
> The inferior doctor treats actual sickness.

Dr. Yen went to Hankow early that summer (1911). There were no trains from Changsha yet, but the rail line from Hankow to Peking was a main thoroughfare, ceaselessly active. He scarcely realized, when he reached Hankow, that he was doing far more than keeping plague out of Central China, important as that was. He was clearing it off the main trunk line that was the highway from north to south. Immediately he persuaded officials and citizens to back his program of action. The railway organized a health service; everyone involved was given immunization with Haffkine's plague vaccine; rat guards were used wherever feasible; and bounties were paid for rats, *per hundred*. It would have been tempting to breed them if they were paid for singly.

The public helped in many ways: scouts were posted at main stations all the way from Peking to Hankow; watchers were in towns along the main cart roads in the north, as well as along the wheelbarrow and coolie roads south of the Yellow River. It was a great campaign, thoroughly organized, and put through by one who was a Chinese leader, fearless, courteous, acceptable to all. He came back to Changsha with well-earned laurels. He had been the leader in the first public-health campaign in Central China.

No sooner was Dr. Yen back at his post than the full blast of the revolution struck Hunan. On October 10, "The Double Tenth" (the tenth day of the tenth month), China burst into flame. Everywhere, except in the north round Peking, the provinces allied themselves with the rebellion. In Hunan we helped to organize Red Cross work. A few months later came the call to set up an antihookworm campaign at the great Pinghsiang colliery, only a few tens of miles away. Dr. Yen went up with a young medical resident, studied the incidence of hookworm among the miners, and reported that the disease could be controlled. We were given the authority to make a thorough survey, and within two years launched a program for eliminating the disease that earned the distinction for the staff of our institution of being preventers as well as curers.

One of the comic aspects of the revolution was the carrying out of orders to the new republican army—"Off with all queues!" It was amusing to watch the reaction of farmers and peasants who came in from the countryside to the city gates carrying their huge loads of rice or vegetables, or trundling their heavy wheelbarrows. The guards rushed out, seized every man's queue, and hacked it off with a sword or clipped it off with huge scissors. For many a man it was like parting with a limb to lose the queue which he had brushed and braided so painstakingly since early boyhood. We saw some of them on their knees, kotowing to the guards as they pled for respite. Others actually fought the soldiers and many tried to run away. Though these farmers became loyal revolutionaries by cutting off their queues, many of them kept an extra queue coiled up inside their skullcaps, ready to let down at a moment's notice if it seemed expedient to renew their allegiance to the Manchu Dynasty. But before the week was out, all the city dwellers and many of the villagers of Central China were largely rid of this mark of Manchu control.

In the hospital, the completely shaved or cropped heads meant less skin disease, less cleaning up before operation. Presently, the authorities issued an edict forbidding women to bind their feet. This long-cherished mark of gentility which had become a tradition with them was a Manchu heritage.

Women who had known nothing since early childhood but the cramping and dwarfing of the bones below the ankle came to the hospital for plastic operations. Many of them were wives of the leading gentry. "We shall not submit any longer to the disgrace of having bound feet. We must have natural feet like our daughters," they would insist. How often during those first months of the republican era did women say to us, "If only we had heeded the counsel of those pioneer missionary women from your country who founded the *T'ien Tsu Hui*—the Natural Foot Association"!

As we looked around the hospital day after day and saw the queues and bound feet disappearing, we noted also that powerful reactionary forces were getting under way and wondered if the sort of democracy for which Dr. Sun had been striving would ever finally emerge. Were there enough men of courage in the land really to free it from the last vestiges of empire? How often, during those fateful days, did Chinese liberals quote the teaching of the ancient sage: "He who sees what is right, and fails to do it, is without courage!"

XX

"SCHOLARS TO WATCH
AND GUARD"

可動天地　一念之誠

Sincerity of purpose can move heaven and earth.

ALTHOUGH we had no appropriate quarters—we were clearly outgrowing the Central Inn—we decided to open the school of nursing which we had planned for a long time.

A trained person to wait on the sick was an entirely new concept in Hunan—so new that we found it necessary to coin a word for "nurse." Miss Nina Gage, who came to Changsha in 1909 to launch the profession of nursing, deferred the opening of the school until she had studied the language for a year. When we opened the school in 1911, she selected "Scholars to Watch and Guard," or, more briefly, "Guard Scholars" as the equivalent of "nurse."

In our advertisements and on the large poster on the wall of the Yali Hospital in West Archway Street we announced:

OPENING OF NEW SCHOOL
BOTH BOYS AND GIRLS TO BE ADMITTED
TRAINING FOR A NEW PROFESSION

"Scholars to Watch and Guard" will be taught in this school. Candidates must have completed two years of Middle School, and must pass the school's entrance examinations successfully. Parents must give their consent, and pay the school fee, as well as a deposit to cover breakage or damage.

Entrance examinations in Chinese and arithmetic will be given in the Yali Hospital on West Archway Street on the fifteenth day of the ninth month.

A woman proctor was engaged and the day set for the examinations. To our delight, twenty girls and forty boys appeared. One or two fell out when they saw the papers. They had not realized that a "Guard Scholar" would need to measure up to so high a standard. Twelve were finally accepted, five girls and seven boys. Miss Gage thought, at first, that the boys were a more promising lot than the girls. Too many problems complicated the lives of the girls. One of them actually came up to the proctor and whispered, "What shall I do about my wedding? It has been set for next summer. The day will soon be fixed by the family after they have consulted the horoscope scholar."

Curious to know what had attracted the girls to the school, I asked one of them, Miss Chu, a tiny thing, barely five feet tall, why she had decided to be a nurse. She told me that she and a friend, Miss Li, were walking past the hospital one day when they saw the poster. They didn't know what this new profession might be, so they went into the hospital to find out. The new proctor, Miss Liu, told them that those who completed the school course successfully would be scholars like any other girls who attended high school in Changsha, but that one of their chief duties would be to watch and guard hospital patients under a doctor's direction.

The girls were puzzled. In China, no one had ever heard of bringing an outsider into a home to help care for a sick person. Mothers or older sisters or hired women were always on hand to attend a patient. Why should an outsider be brought in? Moreover, they said to themselves, a young Chinese girl is brought up for certain definite tasks. In the words of an old Chinese ballad:

> Ten and three, could weave silk threads;
> Ten and four, learned to cut out clothes;
> Ten and five, swept strings of k'ung hou lyre;
> Ten and six, hummed lines of classics: poems, writings;
> Ten and seven, became wife of my lord.

The following day other girls went with them to inquire about the examination. Miss Li had seen her mother in the meantime and was not surprised when she expressed disapproval of the plan. She reminded her that a young girl should be governed by definite rules:

> When walking do not turn the head,
> When speaking do not show the teeth,
> When sitting keep the legs immobile,
> When standing prevent all movement of the skirt.

She was convinced that her mother would never consent to her entering a hospital for study. Who would be on hand to chaperon the girls?

Miss Chu determined to register anyhow. She had always stood well in her classes at Chou Nan School and was sure her mother would relent, provided she got good marks on the entrance examination. If her mother agreed, her father was certain not to object.

Miss Li had almost accepted her mother's adverse decision. She became timid when she heard that boys and girls would attend classes together. She found out, too, that there would be many unpleasant tasks in the wards, tasks that her mother had reminded her were for servants.

The school was a breath-taking innovation for Chinese girls, who had lived in seclusion for centuries. The only men to whom they had been allowed to speak were close relatives. Mothers had always taught their daughters that girlhood was a preparation for marriage and that they must learn all the rituals of the home. In some mysterious way the thought of every girl, mothers said, must be centered on that unknown person to whom she was betrothed. Would he be a scholar of distinction? She hoped so, but in any case she was linked to him by a cord that could not be broken. The cord had been tied even before her birth by the old fairy who arranges marriages.

More than that, all girls were taught that marriage was no indulgence of personal preference; it was the carrying out of a contract made in the beginnings of time by cosmic forces—a contract governed by the stars. No wonder older Changsha mothers were unwilling that their daughters should come out of the seclusion that had been the role of women for centuries!

Nevertheless, these sheltered girls made good pupils. Before long, after they had practised bandaging on each other, they became really proficient. No intern in London or New York could have put on a better dressing or applied a Velpeau bandage more skillfully.

Little by little, parents who had been hesitant at first became delighted that their sons and daughters were doing experiments in chemistry and physics. In China they needed science more, not less. Centuries of unadulterated classics had made generations of Chinese scholars unaccustomed to work with their hands.

On graduation, the nurses changed over to stiff, white uniforms and were held in high respect. Before long the maturer nurses went out with the doctors on serious private cases. The doctor managed to persuade the families to let a trained nurse stay on for a time to make sure that his orders were carried out.

It was not always easy for these girls to go into the homes of strangers, especially those of the officials in which they were too often treated as servants. They suffered many a rebuff, even rude advances, but they stuck to their posts.

One such case, I remember, was that of the governor's son. The governor at this time was a man I thoroughly distrusted. He had been a cruel and corrupt official ever since he had stormed his way in from the north. A hurry call came from the yamen. I went and was challenged at the gate by sentries who carried rifles and mounted bayonets. They looked suspiciously at my calling card and even at the official hospital card.

"Whom does he wish to see?" they asked my chair bearers.

"The foreign doctor has been summoned to the yamen by the *t'ai-t'ai*—the governor's wife. Please let him through quickly, for he has many medical calls to make today!"

"Which *t'ai-t'ai* sent for him?" they shouted back, testing the bearers. "Was it the thin lady or the fat lady?"

I happened to remember, for I had seen her previously. "The fat lady," I called through the front curtain of my sedan chair. They sent a messenger from the gatehouse to the inner apartments to check my claim. The answer came to usher me in.

What a confused picture I found in the apartments of the "fat lady"! She was walking up and down the room distractedly, calling directions to the amah in a harsh, strident voice. "Cover him up more. Why did you open that window? Don't you know that will chill him? Pick him up and carry him in your arms. Put him in the cradle and rock it so long as he whimpers." The orders grew more and more confused.

Suddenly the fat lady caught sight of me. She put on all her party manners, bade me be seated in the guest chair by the window, and called for tea.

"Don't trouble, Madame, to treat me with such 'guest manners,' " I ventured. "Please tell me how long the child has been ill."

"Oh, he is my firstborn son and I am so anxious about his life! He was born five years ago and I haven't been pregnant since. I don't know what the governor will say about me. The thin lady has had two babies since this boy was born and is due to have another in five months. Fortunately for me, her children are both girls. I have the only son. When the governor is in a friendly mood, he says, 'You presented me with a piece of jade!' "

"Yes, Madame," I interjected, "but please tell me when this illness began."

"It began four days ago. The child complained of headache, deep behind the eyes. His fever rose rapidly. You can feel him and see how he is burning up. His face seemed to grow red, and this morning, when daylight came, we saw those little pimples at the top of his forehead. Please tell me, foreign doctor, do you think he will get well? He must get well! He must!"

The mother stood back and gave me room at the side of the bed. The poor little fellow lay there in a bright red satin jacket, with padded jackets beneath it. White would never do in a sickroom. The patient tossed constantly, almost in a delirium. High fever, sure enough. And the rash was plainly that of smallpox.

I told the mother quietly and frankly what his illness was.

No need now to use evasive language. People had come to know that the foreign doctor was particularly careful when his patients were children. I could see that the mother's great fear was that I would want to take her boy to the hospital.

"No," I explained. "We do not admit contagious patients to the hospital if we know about them. Your little boy is very sick. He has the Heavenly Flower Bean sickness. There is no way of stopping this disease in the middle, but we can try to make him more comfortable."

We found a thin red garment with which to cover the boy's chest and hung red curtains in the windows. That I did not insist on white was a relief to the mother. Other orders were given and a little simple medication provided.

"Let me urge you, Madame," I suggested, "to do two things at once. One is to let me vaccinate you and all the attendants immediately. I have the vaccine right here with me. The other is to let me send over one of our young women nurses. They are educated women, trained to take care of the sick and to carry out the doctor's orders. If Miss Li can stay here for three or four days, even a week, you will find how much more comfortable she will make your little son. She is an expert in taking care of sick children."

Both matters required some persuasion. The mother sent a message in to Governor Chang and he appeared at the sick-room within a few minutes. I told him of my proposals. "Above all, sir, you must be vaccinated yourself and have your whole staff protected, too. See that all the grownups and children in the apartments of both ladies are vaccinated immediately. It would be a stain on the governor's reputation if a smallpox epidemic should get started in Changsha because of lack of preventive care here."

"I'll see what I can do," he replied. "I can order the men of the staff and they have to obey me. But what can I do to get the two ladies and all their women servants to listen? You must help me, foreign doctor."

We didn't succeed in vaccinating the entire establishment that afternoon, but we used up the hundred doses of vaccine I had brought along. We isolated the patient and persuaded the governor to keep armed guards at the door of his room. And we installed as nurse in charge, Miss Li Kwei-chên, the same Miss Li who had stopped to read the poster on West Archway Street. She was one of the top-ranking graduates in her class, that first class which pioneered in the establishing of nursing as a profession in Hunan.

XXI

THE STREET OF THE
GRASS TIDE

一日之師

終身為父

Who teaches me for a day is my father for a lifetime.

WITH the opening of the school of nursing and the increased work at the hospital we were growing so rapidly that the Central Inn would no longer house us. There was urgent need of a new building.

On my first furlough in America I told my good Yale classmate, Edward S. Harkness, about it. At his summer home we talked over the entire Changsha medical program. As I inspected the thoroughbred cattle in his model dairies, I wondered how long it would be before our patients in Changsha could have a dependable milk supply. Children throughout China needed milk desperately.

He knew that the medical work was becoming well anchored in Changsha. "I realize," he said, "how much you need a new, adequate hospital out there in China. Have you made any estimate as to what it will cost?" I told him that we had consulted a local engineer from Hankow, had prepared approximate figures of cost, and had made some initial sketches.

"Take those to New York and show them to Gamble Rogers, the architect. Talk the whole thing over with him fully. He will report to me."

From then on, as if by magic, our specifications grew into great rolls of blueprints. I had never dreamed of anything so complete. The plan provided for four hundred hospital beds, with wards reaching out to the south toward the city, only a short distance away, like great arms beckoning the sick to come to us. It would be easy to bring patients out through the Little North Gate.

When the architect asked me about available building materials and the price of labor, I was not caught off guard, for I had brought with me from China samples of all the building materials we might use: the various kinds of woods available in Hunan, bricks, stone, lime, sand, cement.

"These materials," he said, "are most important. They make it possible for me to recommend, without hesitation, that the hospital be of fireproof construction."

Fireproof construction! A reinforced concrete building! I wondered if he knew that nothing like that had ever been thought of in Hunan. I soon found that it was planned to send out a fully qualified engineer, capable of revising the plans and supervising each type of construction.

My next surprise came in a visit with the donor when I discovered that he proposed not only to build the hospital, but also to equip it completely. During our last interview, he said, quietly, but with great earnestness, "There are three conditions I should like to insist upon. The hospital is to be a center of medical education, for my primary concern is not for medical practice only. It is to be a center that the people of Changsha will regard as their own, to manage and to support. It is to be a project for whose current upkeep I am not to be approached."

Nothing could have been wiser. I told him that the one decisive factor in my decision in 1904 to leave India for China had been the sure prospect of starting a university medical school in Changsha.

I wrote at once to Dr. Yen and urged him to take the matter up with Governor T'an and with members of the local gentry who were, by now, such strong friends of ours. "Do see," I wrote him, "whether we can make it a co-operative enterprise from the beginning."

The governor, whom Dr. Yen had recently attended during a severe illness, was enthusiastic about the proposal. By the time I got back to Changsha, Dr. Yen had already organized the local gentry into a Society for the Promotion of Medical Education. They soon obtained permission from Peking to act as the local intermediaries to transmit to the medical college the annual provincial subsidy.

In the summer of 1913, the Yale University Mission in Changsha and the newly constituted Chinese Society for the Promotion of Medical Education set up a joint board with ten members from each group. We were wondering what name to give the new enterprise when our old friend, Mr. Nieh, made a suggestion. "The matter of a name is very important. We are proposing a co-operation between citizens of Hunan and the Yale University Mission. The literary name of our province is Hsiang. The first syllable of the name of the Yali Mission is Ya. Let us call our united body the Hsiangya Medical Educational Association. Everyone who hears that name will recognize that this means Hunan-Yale."

The name conveyed just the meaning we desired. Hsiang was the name of the central river of the province, a waterway of great natural beauty. Our Chinese friends always welcomed a name that savored of mountains or rivers or lakes. The hospital, the medical school, and the school of nursing have, ever since then, been known by the name of Hsiangya.

Finally, after Dr. Yen and I had spent many weeks in Peking that spring of 1914, winning the cabinet members over to our side, we got the Hsiangya agreement ratified. The terms of the agreement were that, in the joint board of managers, the Yale University Mission was to provide the hospital and an agreed number of faculty members for the medical college, while the Hunan Society was to provide the medical college building and an annual sum of fifty thousand dollars, local currency, for running expenses. After an initial period of ten years, both sides would confer, restudy the agreement, and go on with it if satisfactory.

Now that our plans were so well advanced, we did not wait until the completion of the new building to open our medical school. We began to advertise for students in the local papers in Shanghai, Canton, Peking, and Hankow. Entrance examinations were held in those cities before the college opened that fall of 1914. An amazing number of candidates appeared and, in September, we started classes with twenty students. We began in a rented property on the Street of the Grass Tide. Here both hospital wards and teaching laboratories were arranged in a section of the spacious residence of an old grand councilor. Far to the back, where the property touched the enclosure of the Shrine of Old Man Thunder, there was a lovely enclosed garden. Moon gates and latticed windows opened on to the pools and rocky ledges that filled the place. Rare trees and beds of peonies and camellias made it all like a fairyland, sheltered from the world outside of the high surrounding walls.

It was a strange contrast to go out to the front and find ourselves in the prosaic laboratories of chemistry and anatomy. We had always been afraid that the conservative old grand councilor would discover that we had a couple of skeletons in a closet off one of the study halls. At night we kept them under lock and key, for fear the old official might come prowling round to see what was happening on his premises.

These first medical students overcame great difficulties in persuading their parents to let them undertake studies that must have seemed almost a sacrilege, a desecration of the human body. Respect for the dead body was one of the mandates handed down to them by their ancestors. I had feared that reverence for ancestors was so embedded in the thinking of their families that nothing could break it.

The boys came from various backgrounds. T'ang, for instance, was from Liling, a few miles east of Changsha. His schoolboy curiosity had often led him to visit the Pinghsiang collieries, to watch the men bringing coal out of the great shafts. One day when he saw two Chinese visitors at the mines, he bowed to them and made bold to ask what they had in their polished wooden box. They told him it was a microscope. They were going to examine the miners for hookworm as they came off duty. Curious at once, he asked if he could watch them work. "Come along and help us," they suggested.

They showed him how to set up the microscope and to search the specimen for hookworm eggs. When he found the eggs on one slide without help from them, he was delighted. On that day T'ang determined to become a doctor; not merely to treat disease but to study its causes. He asked the older Chinese gentleman, who proved to be Dr. Yen, how he could study scientific medicine. He learned that the Hsiangya Medical College would open its doors at Changsha within a few months. He promised Dr. Yen that day that he would register for the very first class.

Chang's story was quite different. As a boy of twelve he was out with his father in a hillside graveyard where the magistrate had ordered a woman's body to be exhumed. Death had occurred years earlier, during childbirth. The tiny skeleton of the infant was still locked in the mother's skeleton. The father explained to the youth what had happened. It made an unforgettable impression on Chang, and he determined, when he grew up, to be a doctor who could treat women and prevent such tragedies. Five years later when he heard about the opening of the Hsiangya Medical College, he made the three-day overland journey from his home in Liuyang to Changsha to enroll in the premedical class.

Li came from Sianghsiang. He had always planned things a long way ahead. "There are so few medicines," he said, "that really cure disease. I am going to be a research worker. I have often seen how helpless even you teachers seem to be in a serious case. I am going to be an investigator."

These three were typical of the students who began their work in the old councilor's residence. Even there we were cramped and hampered by the sense of restraint that was present everywhere inside the city walls. Both students and teachers were eager to move into the new building and often asked when it would be ready. The teachers hoped that in the new laboratories they would have human anatomical material to teach with. Now that this pioneer band had determined to break with tradition, they were eager to advance. They often spoke of the old Chinese proverb:

Rowing against the current,
One will go either forward or backward.
The boat cannot stand still.

But the anatomy teacher did not wait. One day he called the class together in an inner room, far back from the street. After two of the servants had brought a large trunk into the classroom and left it on the floor, the professor bolted the door carefully. He drew the class round him, and, with the air of a conjurer about to perform some mysterious act, unlocked the trunk. None of the class had ever seen a human cadaver before. They helped the teacher place it on the long table, then stood in hushed excitement as he said, "Gentlemen, today human dissection is to get under way in Hunan!"

The trunk had been shipped up from Shanghai and the customs manifest read "laboratory material." Later in the year, a second trunk, with similar contents, arrived by steamer from Shanghai. The following year, however, political events in Hunan made importing of this sort from Shanghai impossible.

These, however, were not the first anatomical studies in the hospital. Down in old West Archway Street, Goliath, the gateman at the Preparatory School, had understood the need of post-mortem examinations. One day he came to me with a suggestion. "Doctor Hume, you have often said that we should do well to examine a body, to find what disease had caused death. If you will examine the body of my infant son, I shall be grateful. If we know more about his illness, perhaps we can save other children."

I was amazed at his courage and wondered how he could arrange it without causing a commotion. He took his wife to her mother's home for a visit, then returned to the hospital and carried the son's body out to a shed at the back.

Although we had not recognized the child's condition during his lifetime, we found that the liver had become seriously infested with parasites. Our knowledge of tropical disease was greatly enlarged that day.

XXII

THE FAMILY CONTROLS
THE TREATMENT

連心扯胆的
是兒女

It is sons and daughters
That cling to the heartstrings
And pull on the liver.

As THE influence of the hospital spread through the city, we
were called more and more frequently by the families of the
influential old officials who were the aristocracy of Changsha.
The Nieh family who lived in the great mansion on Liuyang
Gate Street was one of these. I had often paid social visits to
the magnificent establishment and enjoyed the flower-decked
courtyards, the gracious reception halls with their stately black-

wood furniture, and the wall paintings on silk scrolls, done in the style of the Sung Dynasty; but on this day I was summoned to see the old official himself, the head of the clan.

Governor Nieh had but recently returned from the highest official posts in two of the seacoast provinces. On account of failing health he had been living quietly at his town house. Brother Four, who had studied English with private tutors in Shanghai, was the son I knew best. He had often talked to me about his father's fainting spells and attacks of nosebleed, so I was not unprepared for this emergency call.

The governor's official sedan chair had been sent to fetch me. We swung in through the great gateway, round the gorgeous dragon screen. In the main reception hall, the seven brothers stood waiting to receive me. All of them greeted me with ceremonial Chinese bows, but Brothers Three and Four, whom I knew so well, shook hands with me also. Brother Three acted as spokesman, addressing me in Chinese, so that all might understand. "Our father was taken ill suddenly. He was walking in the garden, day before yesterday, when he stumbled, fell, and became unconscious at once. He remains unconscious now, and his condition grows more serious every hour. Two of the most distinguished physicians in Hunan, Doctor Wang and Doctor Lei, have already examined him. Both of them agree that the outlook is exceedingly grave. Brother Four and I persuaded our five brothers to send for you. As you probably know, they have great confidence in Chinese medicine. We two believe that Western medicine also should be tried for our father. Will you go with us and examine him in the inner bedroom?"

Following Brother Three and accompanied by the other six, I made my way to the patient's room. He was propped up by two servants who sat beside him on the bed. This was a universal practice, it being believed that the more fully supine a

patient lay in bed, the worse the outlook. Everything was done
to persuade the body and spirit to stay together. To have the
patient lie quite flat would be to invite dissolution.

The diagnosis was evident the moment I entered the darkened room: slow, stertorous breathing, deep coma. Undoubtedly there was a ruptured blood vessel in the brain.

I took my place by the patient and examined the pulse carefully and long, first on the left wrist, then on the right. Tongue,
pupils, extremities, loss of muscular power, and all the other
signs were noted. I observed that the seven brothers were all
quite impressed with my care, especially with my detailed observations of tongue and pulse. They were glad, too, that I
was using the thermometer. I heard them comment to each
other as they saw me record my findings on a history card.
When I was through, the spokesman asked whether I had
made a diagnosis.

"Your father has had a stroke of apoplexy—*chung fêng*, you
call it."

With one voice, the seven brothers called out, "Correct!"

Clearly they were the jury—I merely a witness put on the
stand. It was my first vivid lesson as to the complete control
by a Chinese family over diagnosis and decision.

"What procedure do you recommend?" the spokesman continued.

"You understand that this 'stroke' is undoubtedly due to a
breaking of one of the arteries in the brain. We should do all
we can to reduce the pressure of his pulse."

That caused a commotion. "Who ever heard of weakening
the pulse strength in a dangerously ill patient?" one of the conservative brothers challenged. "A strong pulse is the one sure
guarantee of life."

At this point Brother Four broke in. He and I had become
good friends, with great mutual confidence in each other. "Per-

haps," he said, "Doctor Hume has some classical authority for his position!"

I was grateful enough, both for the championing of my cause and, more particularly, for the fact that I had taken along in my medical bag, as always, a Chinese translation of Osler's *Practice of Medicine*. I turned to the relevant page and handed the book over. Sir William Osler never had more attentive readers than those seven brothers, two ready to accept the dicta of a Western physician, and the other five skeptical, almost scornful.

They read of the procedure I was recommending: the head was to be lowered, the body to be kept warm, a high enema to be given.

"Will you not prescribe some drug?" the spokesman inquired, hopeful that I, his nominee, would not undermine his family's confidence in me. He wanted me to do something really dramatic.

I wrote a prescription for a purgative, and described it to them carefully. They knew all about mercury as a cathartic for they had read about it in the writings of their own physicians. Yet the decision lay, not with this jury, but with their mother, who was now the final arbiter. The prescription was taken back to the women's apartments by Brother Four, who returned presently, elated that he had persuaded her to approve both the drug and the entire course of action I had outlined. I gave some further instructions, promised to send over a hospital orderly as soon as possible, and bowed my way out to the great front gate. In the front courtyard I turned to bow again and be bowed to by the seven brothers. Two of them, at least, were particularly grateful for my visit.

Brother Four escorted me personally to the sedan chair and said that he would count on seeing me often, both professionally and as a personal friend. "You must not let the conservatism here discourage you. I hope our mother will be willing to have your orderly come over and stay here to carry out all your instructions. I fear my father will not survive this stroke, but we know you have done all that was possible."

Governor Nieh died three days later, but our friendship with the family continued unbroken. I received the formal invitations to the public service of mourning and responded by sending the conventional white scrolls, inscribed with tribute phrases honoring the deceased leader. This was the correct way to express condolence.

The brothers all wore coarse hempen mourning robes, and strands of coarse hempen thread were braided into their queues, to remain for three full years. There was no feasting during those years; the mother and her seven sons, as well as the several daughters, remained quietly at home.

In China death came, like everything else, as part of a predestined cycle; night following day, new moon following full moon, winter coming after summer, death after life. Mourning was not a mere show, with sacrifice and wailing, with unbleached cotton garments and abstemiousness; it was a true liturgy of the oneness of life, deliberately adopted and observed through the years, commemorating the beauty and dignity of continuing existence, with its alternating cycles of shadow and light.

When Mr. Liang, the provincial treasurer, fell ill, his son came in person to escort me to see his father professionally. When he first entered the hospital reception room, I didn't realize what a unique experience lay ahead of me. He spoke with directness. "My father has been ill a long time. Just a week ago he took a serious turn for the worse, so my mother is now willing to have you called in. I tried to get my family to let me bring you two months ago, but you know how conservative older Hunan people are. Until today they thought that Doctor Wang understood Father's symptoms well enough."

Dr. Wang, I knew, was the most distinguished Chinese physician in Changsha. "How long has he been in charge of your father?" I asked.

"What do you mean, been in charge?"

Again I had forgotten that no doctor ever had final authority.

How frequently had my sedan chair been on the way out from the compound of a mandarin's residence, only to run into another sedan chair on its way in, carrying some well-known Chinese doctor as the next consultant on the case. I imagined that, in this case, the usual routine would be followed; that I would come, look the patient over, ask the necessary questions, make my examination and suggestions, and then withdraw. But, instead, at the door of the palatial home, the sedan chairs entered the court together, Dr. Wang's and mine. Together we were shown into the reception room, and the servants placed us side by side on the splendid, carved black wooden settee at the head of the room. Steaming cups of fragrant jasmine tea were brought in, and we were served simultaneously. Presently, the two older sons of the patient came in, made profound bows to each of us, then sat one on either side of the reception hall.

"Our father is very ill," the older brother said, "and we have persuaded our mother to let us invite you both together, so that we may have the benefit of a consultation between representatives of two systems of medicine. We hope you will do our family the honor of examining the patient together, and giving us your joint opinion about him. So far as we know, this is the first time that two such eminent doctors have been invited to a home in Changsha together. We believe that in our new China both Western and Chinese systems of medicine should be fully explored. By these means we should have a better understanding of the causes of disease and a far wider range of remedies to draw upon."

I scarcely knew who was the more surprised, Dr. Wang or I, but we bowed our acceptance of the unprecedented proposal and followed the brothers into the sick man's room. The patient was unconscious, yet was propped up in bed by two menservants. I appreciated the courtesy shown by these brothers —both trained in a modern university—who appeared to be calling for a consultation; yet I was pretty sure it was I, the newcomer, who was being put to the test. The family would watch me very closely, to see how near my diagnosis might come to that of Dr. Wang's.

Partly because I was the younger, but largely in order to give me more time to observe the patient and to study Dr. Wang's procedures, I bowed and asked him to examine the patient first. It was a great experience to watch him. He sat down on a chair at the left side of the patient's bed, facing him, and gazed long and searchingly at his head, the face and neck puffed with edema; there was marked venous pulsation in his neck.

Up to this time Dr. Wang had not put his hands on the patient. Now he bent over, listening for every possible sound: the irregular breathing, the low moaning.

Then he began his questions. How long had the patient been ill? Was it a first or a renewed attack of the malady? Had he been exposed to great dampness or cold? Had there been any family conflict before the onset of the illness? After a few further inquiries, Dr. Wang came close to the bed. He moved with great precision and solemnity. The servants placed a pile of books, about three inches high, near his hand; the doctor laid the patient's left wrist gently on the books and felt the pulse long and thoughtfully. Then the right wrist was brought across the body and, as carefully as before, the pulse was felt on this side as well. He scrutinized the patient's tongue, then his eyes, after opening the lids that were tightly pressed together.

Now it was my turn. Dr. Wang asked me to examine the patient. I went through the form of examination that a Western physician would follow with a patient in coma, feeling the pulse, examining the pupils, the tongue, the reflexes, and using stethoscope and thermometer. I even managed to have the sleeve raised and to take the blood pressure, which was alarmingly high. Then I took my seat, too, in one of the guest chairs.

As I had yielded place to Dr. Wang in making the examination, so now I ventured to ask him, as the senior, to state what his diagnosis might be.

He answered at great length, giving me a learned discourse about the various possibilities that might account for the coma. "Finally," he observed, "you saw the care with which I examined the three pulse points on the left wrist, and the three on the right wrist. We have learned the art of the pulse from the teachings of Wang Shu-ho, who lived during the Chin Dynasty. He taught that the ultimate nature of any disease could be discovered by an exhaustive study of the two pulses. If you will feel the left pulses for yourself, Foreign Doctor, you will find that the uppermost of the three pulses there, the one nearest the elbow, has practically disappeared; even the first or lowest pulse, the one nearest the fingers, is scarcely to be felt. These observations, together with long experience and attention to the teaching of the great medical sages, have convinced me that our patient has serious disease of the kidneys.

There is also considerable involvement of the heart. I beg of you to repeat my examination and to say whether you confirm my findings."

The patient's entire body was swollen and edematous. I could press deeply into the tissues anywhere and leave a great dent behind. My examination had already led me to an independent diagnosis; but, out of respect to the older physician, I felt the two wrists again, then answered quietly that I was inclined to agree with his conclusion. I added that I would reserve final judgment until certain laboratory tests had been made. Later on, the tests confirmed his conclusion.

Dr. Wang had drunk deeply at the springs of Chinese medicine but had never witnessed a post-mortem examination or made a chemical or microscopic test in the laboratory. Yet his verdict was given with assurance. I could almost hear him add, "What else could it be but kidney disease?"

A look at the faces of the brothers was enough to demonstrate their trust in their own doctor. They were unquestionably reassured to find the foreign doctor agreeing with their own distinguished physician.

As we walked out to the front together, I said to Dr. Wang, "You must do our hospital the honor of an early visit to its wards and laboratories. I feel sure you would be interested to see under the microscope a section showing kidney disease."

"Thank you for the kind suggestion. It would be most interesting. I fear I should not understand it at all. Our conception of the nature of disease is so different from yours in the West."

When I repeated the invitation to visit the laboratory and see tests for kidney disease as well as many other conditions, I added that our young medical students did these tests with great accuracy. Dr. Wang commented that he hoped we did not let the students forget the names and the teachings of their own Pien and Chang, the great early physicians, and of Wang Shu-ho, the renowned authority on the pulse.

I took the hint and invited him to lecture on their teachings once each term. He promised to come, and we parted good friends. On the trip home as I thought back to the visit, I was grateful that I had met such a representative of the old school of medicine and had examined a patient with him. Two days later Treasurer Liang died in coma, all the signs confirming the diagnosis of kidney disease made by Dr. Wang.

Many friendships grew up with these Changsha families through the years. Every now and then one of them, grateful for the recovery of a well-loved child, would present a splendid black-lacquered panel to the hospital, to be hung high on the walls of the main corridor where admiring visitors could read it. The panel, often in gold-lacquered characters a foot high, proclaimed the medical or surgical skill of this or that doctor on the staff.

These panels were often carried to the hospital in a procession accompanied by a band and the sound of exploding firecrackers. One day we met at the front door a procession carrying something that looked like a long table-top, covered with a splendid piece of embroidery. This panel was the gift of old Dr. Chu, a member of the Hsiangya board who had become so appreciative of the skill of our surgeons that he compared them to the master surgeon of Chinese history. The panel read:

Shu Ch'ao Hua T'o.

Skill excelling Hua T'o.

Another procession came with a panel sent by Colonel Ch'ên, expressing gratitude for the recovery of his son who had been desperately ill with pneumonia. The characters read:

The Great Temple at Nan Yo

The Hsiangya Hospital

Hui Shêng.

Life has returned.

Still another was the gift of our police commissioner, one of our stanchest supporters. His panel read:

Lai Su.

You have come to revive.

XXIII

DR. WELCH LAYS THE CORNERSTONE

樂 方 有
乎 來 朋
　 不 自
　 亦 遠

To have friends come from afar, is this not true joy?

Not long after we moved to the Street of the Grass Tide we turned the first sod for the new hospital on our beautiful site outside the North Gate. A broad avenue, fully a hundred feet wide, had been laid out by the city, extending from the Hsiang River half a mile to the west, past our front entrance, to the east of the city, where the railroad would soon be running. Just across the avenue the academic college campus was bustling with building activity. We hoped that buildings on both sides of the avenue would be ready for use in the fall of 1916.

Off across the river, a little to the south, Yolu Shan rose in its spring cloak of pink azaleas. It was the time of the year when that view of the mountain was always most beautiful. Our Chinese friends, leaders of the Changsha gentry who had come to attend the ceremony, commented, as we looked across the river to the mountains beyond, "You are favored by heaven and have excellent fêng-shui here. The spirits of wind and water are all on your side."

One amusing episode occurred that afternoon. Among the Chinese members of the Hsiangya board, none was more enthusiastic than Dr. Chu, versed in the medical lore of old China, and yet a seeker, from his earliest years, after new knowledge. During the war with the French in 1885 he had served as an army physician, practising the old medicine, needling, applying plasters, and all that; but always trying, after the treaty was signed, to meet French medical officers and pick up what he could of modern medicine. There was no keener spirit among the Chinese trustees than he. In fact, the purchase of the whole medical property, on which hospital and medical school were to be erected, had been his chief concern.

On this afternoon Dr. Chu came to me on the sidelines and whispered, "Why didn't you have the boundary stones moved twenty or more feet farther back all round? I gave you weeks of interval after the payment was made, before it was necessary to take the deeds down to the yamen to be stamped officially. You might easily have enlarged the property quite a bit. The measurements were purposely left a trifle indefinite and it would not have been an unusual procedure."

Huang Laopan, who had mended my son's orthodontic apparatus and could do anything whether it was mending bits of gold wire or building a college dormitory, was to be the chief contractor and building superintendent. It was agreed that he should do the work on a cost-plus basis. We were to furnish the steel and cement for the fireproof construction, and he was to hire the workmen. There would be detailed records kept in the office of works.

One day we heard the sounds of feasting over in the workmen's dormitory. Till then we had not realized that we were to have an added partner in the work, Lu Pan, the patron of carpenters. No one would think of starting a new building in China without spreading a feast in his honor. Paper money was burned outside the shed, incense and firecrackers lighted, just to make sure that Lu Pan was on the carpenters' side as they began work.

The site was quickly leveled off, then, after working with compass and level for days, the American engineer and Huang Laopan marked out the lines for the first foundation trenches. Tomorrow, the contractor promised, they would start digging the trenches. Huge piles of broken stone were lying ready on every side.

But tomorrow came and went, and the day after that as well. No workmen were to be seen on the site. We had completely forgotten how dangerous it was to disturb the earth in China and that disturbed spirits might easily do damage to any building. So we sent for Huang Laopan.

"Wasn't it agreed that the main trenches were to be started two days ago? Has there been a strike among the workmen?"

"No, sir, there has been no strike. But," and his face fell, "they refused to lift a single pickaxe until old Ma, the soothsayer, had consulted the oracles and fixed on an auspicious day. They'll be starting in a day or two."

"But we thought you were a Christian. Why should you let your men be turned aside just because of an old popular belief?"

"Well, you see, sir, although I am a church member, very few of the workmen are. They have never in their lives commenced any building operation without consulting the oracles. We must not use threats. Don't forget, sir, that many of these workmen have been a bit timid about working on a foreign building. They wouldn't like to feel, for example, that working on this foreign hospital made it necessary for them to lose their confidence in Chinese medicine. I don't believe they will want to switch over to Western medicine yet. They are much more likely to work faithfully with us if we don't interfere with their old customs and prejudices."

Two days later several hundred workmen were there, and the excavation went ahead. Western builders would have thought engines and bulldozers essential, but human labor was all-sufficient in China, whether for foundation work or highway construction. Every workman had all he needed, a mattock and hoe and a pair of tiny baskets to carry off the excavated dirt.

One morning a strange sight met our eyes as we walked over to inspect the new construction. Over there, where the hospital was supposed to be going up, we saw what looked like a grove of flowering young trees, springing up out of the walls that were now a foot above ground. Again we referred to Huang Laopan to inquire the meaning of this forest.

"We knew you wouldn't mind, sir. It is an old custom in China. We have already disturbed the ground here by digging this enormous excavation, so the workmen have tied bunches of young pine branches to the tops of the scaffolding poles, hoping the aggrieved earth spirits will think they are looking down on a grove of trees and will pass by without doing us injury."

We thought it better not to interfere. A few days later we found another pole standing out between two of the wells, a basketwork sieve tied to its top and a mirror hung in the middle. One of the workmen explained that good influences could pass through the sieve and help them. The mirror transformed every adverse influence into good fortune.

Often, through the months of construction, we heard the chanting of Taoist priests over in the workmen's dormitory.

Perhaps they were intoning prayers to their patron saint. Would Lu Pan protect us, we wondered, when we installed the electric pump in the deep well we were digging?

By the fall of 1915 we were ready for the next ceremony. During the summer I wrote and urged Professor William H. Welch of Johns Hopkins, my old teacher, to visit Changsha in October. I told him we should have a festive occasion if only he would come and lay the cornerstone. He knew the donor well, and wrote back: "Dear Hume, I have never laid a cornerstone in my life, but I am perfectly willing to try."

The party of visitors, Dr. Welch, Dr. Simon Flexner, and others, reached Changsha on October 17 and were busy people for two days. They spent a large portion of their time in our hospital on the Street of the Grass Tide, inspecting each ward, public and private, the operating rooms, the library. But for Dr. Welch the laboratory was the center of interest. We begged him to examine and describe for us a greatly enlarged spleen which one of our surgeons had just removed. No one who was with him that afternoon will ever forget the eagerness of the scientist as he studied the specimen. As he went out of the door, he said, "I shall think it over and tell you, before I leave Changsha, what my conclusions are."

On the morning of the eighteenth we took the party across the river to climb Yolu Shan, our favorite mountain, known as the "Mountain of the Three Religions." We showed them the spreading Confucian temple at the base, designed to be visited by scholars who were seeking, in the old days, to pass the classical provincial examinations; the Buddhist monastery halfway up; and the Taoist temple at the top, with its glorious outlook through the Gate with the View of the Hsiang. One could see up the river valley for nearly thirty miles.

As we entered the temple, the venerable chief priest came out and greeted Dr. Welch and his colleagues with profound bows. "How old are you, revered sir?" he asked Dr. Welch.

Without a moment's hesitation the doctor, who was white-haired but not at all old-looking, flashed back, "I am a hundred and fifty-six years old." The other American guests, happily, gave no sign of their surprise, but the Taoist priest, not accustomed to such visitors, bowed again and again and asked me to convey to Dr. Welch his profound gratitude that his temple had been thus honored.

"Revered sir," he said, "I should like to hang in the corridors of your house a lacquered tribute panel saying: 'Visitor from across the sea, I honor you as a medical forefather.'"

That afternoon, October 18, we celebrated the laying of the cornerstone. The splendid granite block hung suspended, ready for the trowel and mortar, with the name of the hospital and the date carved deep into the stone in Chinese and English characters. Before the stone was lowered, Dr. Welch made the chief address of the day. He referred to the fact that, in 1854, the first Chinese student to go abroad, Yung Wing, had received his bachelor's degree at Yale; that he, himself, had received his own degree there in 1870. An occasion like this, he said, marked one of those great moments when science and humanity, permeated by the spirit of religion, reached out and joined hands across the sea. There could be no interfering boundaries of race or creed in such an institution. He told the audience of the three conditions laid down by the donor of the hospital and added that, so soon as he should return to America, he would tell him of this occasion in Changsha as a happy omen of the way in which those conditions were already being met.

That night we took the visiting party to the steamer for Hankow. While we were still standing on the dock, waving to the guests on the deck, Dr. Welch leaned over the rail and called out, "Oh, Hume, I have been thinking about that spleen.

I am sure it was a case of chronic passive congestion!" Truly the farewell words of a pathologist!

The cornerstone of modern medical practice and education, the goal of my life in China, was now well and truly laid.

XXIV

OUTSIDE THE CITY WALL

温故而知新
可以為師矣

He who looks back to the old
And knows the new
Is worthy to be a scholar.

WITH the building of the new hospital, the time had come
for us to leave the strange little house in which our family had
lived for so many years. Each tiny courtyard had become familiar, even the hole in our back wall, that Great Peace Door
through which we escaped on the night of the rice riots. The
firewalls had shut out the noise and confusion of neighbors
and city thoroughfares. Now we were going to live "outside
the North Gate."

The great city wall had come to be like sheltering arms about us. What we had thought of with apprehension on that memorable day, years earlier, when we first landed off the steamer at Changsha, had become our friend and guardian. In and out, through its massive gates, we had passed during those first dozen years, starting on journeys or social visits but, more frequently, on medical calls. Many were the summons that took me, usually in some emergency, to see an injured man or a patient ill with malaria or typhoid. Not a few were obstetrical cases over on the wooded island in the middle of the river.

As our sedan chairs passed through the North Gate that late summer afternoon, we wondered how we should ever have the courage to sleep outside the wall, exposed and unprotected. Especially at night, we seemed out there to be nearer the meeting place of human beings and the spirit world.

On the other side of death lay the world of Yin in which the ghosts of an earthly existence had the same needs that were felt by them here on earth in the world of light, the Yang world. Everywhere in China people seemed conscious of the nearness of the spirits. The soul that had left its body was sure to be hovering near. It was essential to provide that wandering spirit with everything it might need.

To the graveyards we saw members of the family bringing the symbols of need that were to be sent up to the spirit world in flames. One of the strangest graveyards we knew was just south of the new hospital. It consisted of layer upon layer of ancient mounds, superimposed one above the other like an ancient manuscript with a new record inscribed above an older one. The lowest layer of graves, men told us, dated back fully three thousand years.

Thin columns of smoke rose frequently from some more recent grave. We often watched processions of mourners on their way to this cemetery. In front marched men who scattered shining silver paper coins. This was the "road cash" with which they hoped to buy the favor of malicious imps, to keep them from molesting the departed spirit.

Behind them followed mourners carrying paper figures, including, almost always, figures of cranes with outspread wings, emblems of long life. It was a common belief that the burning of images of the crane would make it possible for the departed spirit to ride upon its back to the upper world.

Most frequently they carried a paper house, quite perfect in its detail. Rickshas or sedan chairs stood in front at its gate. Inside were tables and chairs, cupboards and stoves, all beautifully designed. In every part of this paper house, designed for the departed spirit, we saw the mourners scattering paper coins. In the world of shadows he should have no need that spirit money would not provide for. When all the paper figures had gone up in smoke we could see an expression of satisfaction on the faces of the mourners. What they had done was sure to bring them into closer accord with the spirits in that other world. They never thought that there was a great gulf fixed between themselves and the world of shadows.

There were no vacant spaces in the countryside where we had come to live. Every foot of ground was either rice field or vegetable garden or a patch of graves. Right in the middle of the college campus the Ho family had its little family hill of gravemounds, each with an appropriate carved slab of granite. We talked about buying the plot, about a ceremony to move those ancient graves to another spot; but the family never quite agreed. Why should they disturb the spirits of their ancestors to accommodate a foreign school? However, that low hill of graves, reaching right up to the college chapel, never disturbed the students. They went on with their games unmindful of the presence of the spirits.

On the hospital grounds we had even more trouble. Several times court action was brought against us for having trespassed ever so little on the enclosure of the graves of this family or that. A good deal of money was spent by the hospital in reconciling ourselves with the living descendants of those whom we had unwittingly dishonored.

It was an undertaking now to get into the city if medical calls summoned me at night. Whenever I came up to the barred gates and peeped through the crack between, I would pound and shout, "*K'ai mên!*—Open the gate!"

Finally, the gatekeeper's sleepy voice would call out feebly, "Come tomorrow. The gate is locked for the night."

"No," I would shout. "No, I have a pass from the governor, authorizing me to come in for a medical visit."

"Oh you have, have you? Let's see it! Push the pass through the crack. No, wait a moment, stand there and let the light of your lantern fall on your face so we'll be able to see if you are really the foreign doctor."

Then a long wait, as the guards scrutinized me through the crack. After they recognized that I was really what I claimed to be there would be still more waiting while my pass was taken up to the office of the commandant. Finally, permission was given and the huge beam that served as a crossbar was lifted down. Sometimes it took the combined efforts of three strong men to lift one end of that beam off its bracket and swing it round so that the gate could be opened wide enough to admit a pedestrian. There was always much more commotion if we were a party in sedan chairs and the gate had to be opened wider.

Life outside the wall did not make us less near to the old China with its awareness of the continuity of all life. This visible existence, everyone knew, was only a span, a bit of transitory existence, in the endless continuing march of the race.

Yet out here in the country, there was a sense of something new, something coming into being. No longer were we cramped by the old. From our windows we could look out and see the new life emerging. There was the school athletic field, right before our eyes, with boys pole-vaulting and jumping and running. Every week teams came to the grounds from other schools in the city and from schools in Hankow. Now and again the school team would play with a team from an American gunboat that had come up the river on its winter journey to Changsha. The antics of the cheer leaders would have startled the gentry of an older generation. All the staid deportment of the ancient scholar had gone. Outside the city wall we were in the presence of a new China.

Girl students, too, a new generation of them, came running by with unbound feet. From one and another school near by they came over to our athletic field and took part in volleyball and other contests. They had close-cropped hair and wore athletic shorts. They were the girls who would usher in the new China. They would measure up to the tradition of the heroines of Hunan if an enemy should ever invade their beloved province.

One of these girl students was T'ang Kwei-lin. Years later we learned that when war came she donned a soldier's uniform and was able, disguised as a man, to endure all the fatigue of the ordinary foot soldier. She joined an infantry unit that moved straight into action against the Japanese invaders. She faced death constantly, especially after joining the dare-to-die battalion that was ordered to defend a mountain garrison near the Long River. Here she fought desperately for many hours, till two bullet wounds put her out of action. Peasants carried her for miles to a base hospital. Only then was it discovered that she was a girl. When she begged to be allowed to rejoin her fighting comrades, this was refused. She was told that such Hunan heroines were needed behind the lines for national reconstruction work.

Each spring there was something more outside the city wall than the bursting into bloom of azaleas and forsythia, "the flower that welcomes the spring." Medical students and others on our grounds regularly organized themselves into bands and went out on a Saturday afternoon or Sunday to volunteer as teachers. They had heard "Jimmy" Yen tell of his methods when he came to Changsha to make the first test of his program of mass education. He had brought groups together in schools and in banks, in shops and in guild halls, and trained them to carry the program of literacy to everybody. His first experiment in Changsha was such a conspicuous success that a national movement for mass education was launched, and spread like wildfire throughout China.

It was an amazing thing to go down to some hall that had been loaned for the occasion and see those student teachers, surrounded by groups of ricksha pullers or farmers, shop apprentices or other illiterates, while they taught them to read, using chart and diagram and the printed page. Spring had come indeed for these who had always lived a limited existence, cramped by the old traditions which provided them no opportunity to learn to read and write.

Old Wu nai-nai was a symbol of a thousand grandmothers. She had never been to a hospital when *her* babies were born; but now when her joints creaked or her pulse hammered too loud she came for treatment. She learned to read in the wards, with modern nurses as her teachers. Revitalized and eager for life, this woman with twelve grandchildren went back to her village healed in body and with a mind that had moved *outside* the gates of old conservative tradition. *She* would have *her* daughter come to the modern hospital to have her babies. Her granddaughters would play all the school games with unbound feet and unfettered minds. She was part of the new China.

But at one season every year, during the festival of the Chinese New Year, new China was forgotten. People went back to customs that were centuries old. To go into the walled city on medical visits on New Year's morning was a unique experience. Coolies refused payment for their services, though they were willing to pull rickshas or carry sedan chairs. It would not do to be *reckoned* as working on the great holiday. Right up to noon there were men going about with lighted lanterns. "All debts," the chair bearers told me, "must be collected *before* New Year's Day." So the pretence was made by these men, who appeared to be searching for something with their lanterns, that it was still the night before.

The national holidays of the Westerner, all taken together, do not begin to mean to us what the New Year's festival means to China. Feasting takes the place of thrift, even for the poorest. Families that have been separated are reunited. Everyone gives himself up to a measure of fun. They are celebrating rebirth, the rebirth of all life, when heaven begins to prepare the soil for the crop that must feed the nation, when men settle up their accounts, both with their own fellows and with the spirit world.

Every household at this season had a messenger who went to the spirit world to report. Tsao Wang, the kitchen god, was hearth god and celestial spy all in one. A niche behind the kitchen stove was his shrine in every home. That tiny recess, black with smoke, held a gaudy picture of His Highness, and even the cockroaches assembled there were known as the "horses of Tsao Wang." At the appointed time his image was burned, releasing his spirit for the journey to the other world.

Just before the hour of the kitchen god's departure, offerings of sweet food were made, including a confection of sticky rice. With this smeared on his lips, the family might depend on him to report only flattering things about them; nothing about the carelessness that let Brother Number Two catch the dreadful cold that was nearly the end of him, or about the gossip and rattle-brained chatter that gave old grandmother a stroke in the tenth month. After Tsao Wang's noisy send-off with hundreds of tiny sputtering firecrackers, the tension in the kitchen was eased.

> Once the cat's away,
> The mice climb over the bamboo fence.

Year after year we saw the New Year's urge take possession of the hospital. Wards were completely emptied. Even the seriously ill suddenly had an access of new strength that enabled them to go home. Surgical operations on New Year's Day? Never! There was almost a week of rest for surgical assistants and nurses. They, too, could have reunions with their families, wear their gay clothes, and go calling on their friends.

Often, when we came back through the city gates at night, we saw long shafts of light piercing the darkness from the obstetrical delivery room. Here again was the new China where scientific medicine would not pause when an emergency rose, even though it was New Year's. Women had begun to learn about prenatal clinics. They were discovering something better than throwing open their cupboard doors and box lids when birth was at hand. They, too, had come to live outside the city wall.

XXV
THE WORLD OF SPIRITS

Man cannot do anything without the spirits.

In the old city and outside the walls, everywhere about us we were conscious of the world of spirits and of how intimately they dwelt with the living. These pictures have stayed with me.

The Mother. It was nearly dark as we hurried back from our walk along the top of that straight stretch of the Changsha wall, north of *Ts'ao Ch'ao Mên*, Gate of the Grass Tide. They always closed the barriers at the side of the gate at sunset, and we were racing to get through. Suddenly, we heard the sound of a woman's voice crying out, "Oh, my child, *Er Pao*, come back. Little one, return home!"

The woman's home was a mud plaster lean-to, standing in the alley just inside the city wall. As dusk fell she had come out into the tiny street and was pacing back and forth past the house, utterly unconscious of the people watching her. "Come

back, my child, come home! The house is swept, your clothes
are ready, the bed is waiting." Over and over again she wailed
aloud, while day turned to dusk, and dusk to darkness. It was
a cry of anguish, begging the sick child's soul to come home.

As we watched, the frightened mother ran up a ladder to a
little ledge beside the house and began to wave a bamboo pole,
to one end of which a child's garment was fastened. Over and
over she called, "*Er Pao*, come back home!" Then another
member of the family appeared in the tiny alley, beating a
gong loudly as if to get the attention of the missing soul. While
crowds gathered to watch, the mother went on wailing, "*Er
Pao*, come back! Your clothes are ready for you! Come home!"

Teacher Liu told us that, when the baby became unconscious, the mother had tried to coax it back to consciousness.
Failing to revive it, she went outside the house and called for
the infant's missing soul to return. Over and over again she
waved its garments in the air, hoping that the absent spirit
would return from its journey, recognize its own clothes, and
slip quietly into them. The mother firmly believed that the
child's *shên*, its higher spirit, had left the body and that she
was the intermediary to link soul and body.

"You may be sure," Teacher Liu told us, "that every time
a mother brings an unconscious child to you she has already
done all in her power to plead with its soul to return. She
comes to the foreign doctor only because she finds her own
efforts unavailing."

Vespers. The young apprentice came out from the depths
of the shop just as darkness fell. He put up the boards, one after
another, closing the place in for the night. Then, just before
barring the door, he appeared again, reverently carrying three

lighted sticks of incense. Facing the darkened street, he repeated a prayer that had come down through the centuries,
bowed solemnly three times, facing to the left, straight forward, and to the right. Thus heaven and earth and man were
invoked to bear witness that the protection of the unseen
world had been sought. The three incense sticks, still glowing
faintly, were inserted into a little bracket high up on one side
of the entrance; then the worshiper went inside, concluding
the ceremony by the final barring of the door. Nothing would
now disturb the occupants within, save, perhaps, the tinkling
bell of the itinerant food vender. His wares might be bought
through that lesser opening at the lower part of the door. Evil
spirits were now warned away. Heaven was on the side of the
household for the night.

Bells and Prayers. A gentle tinkling of bells, accompanied
by a sort of droned incantation, caught my ear as I walked
along a narrow Changsha street one day. My companion told
me that priests inside the house we were passing were saying
prayers for the recovery of a sick member of the family. In a
wealthy home, he said, there would surely be relays of priests
on duty to keep the prayers going night and day. I asked him
whether the priests were Buddhists or Taoists.

"Either kind," he said. "You know them apart, don't you?
The Buddhist priests wear long saffron-colored robes and have
their heads clean-shaven. If you look carefully you will see six
circular marks branded on each priest's scalp, three on a side.
These are the signs of his permanent acceptance into the priest-
hood, burned in when he is through his novitiate. The Taoist
priests wear a long dark-blue robe, and have a band round the
head topped by a sort of formal cap. They do not shave their

heads. There are many of them in the temple on top of Yolu Shan, across the river."

I asked him if a doctor wouldn't be more useful, and he answered, "In every home when illness comes, the first instinct of the family is to do something; above all, not to sit idle. Even when a doctor has been in attendance, there are long hours when he is not at hand. Everyone believes that the way to expel illness is to use the old, tried herb remedies, and drive out the evil spirits by prayer. The tinkling of the bells you hear is but a sign that people are actually seeking the help of the unseen world of spirits. The bells are meant to waken the good spirits and bring their aid."

"Is that all the priests do—strike bells and recite incantations?"

"No, they often write charms, painting huge characters or grotesque figures of mythical animals on squares of paper. These are hung on the doors and walls of the sickroom. Sometimes they order a cock to be killed and its body put up over the door. You see, the cock is supposed to frighten disease away as well as darkness."

Temples. The surest place of approach to the unseen spirits was the temple, either a tiny one at some unimportant street corner or a great solemn, vaulted one, like the Temple of the Ruler of the City down near the southeast corner of the wall. The priests there could be counted on for a cure.

As we stood watching one day, the trembling mother of a sick boy threw down a couple of coppers in front of the great altar, lighted a tiny candle and a stick of incense, and placed both in the big bronze urn. A waiting priest came over and asked what favor she sought. After she told him, he stood beside her, shook a lacquered cylinder crowded full of numbered bamboo tallies and picked up the first tally to fall out. "Here you are. This tally is number 97. Wait till I see whether it bears the answer you seek."

He consulted the gourds and the answer was negative. When he shook the cylinder again, tally number 102 fell out. Again the gourds gave a negative response. But at the third test the gourds confirmed the number. "Now we know this is your answer," he assured her. "Take this prescription and have it filled at the big drug shop at the corner of Nan Mên Chêng Chieh. Give the medicine to the sick child at once. The spirits promise that it will bring what you desire."

Off the fearful mother hurried, a little gleam of hope lighted within. Was not the Ch'êng Huang Miao the most honored of all the Changsha temples?

One day the worshiper I watched was a childless woman. She had been married for years, yet her prayer for a child had never been answered. She now made her vows to Kuan Yin, the goddess of mercy, who heeds the petitions of childless women. Praying, she promised everything: if it were a son, that he should become a monk; if a daughter, that she should become a nun; she herself would gladly live in poverty all her days if only she might have a child. The listening priest went through the ritual and gave her a prophetic slip. "Yes, you will have a child if you go on foot as a pilgrim to the southern sacred mountain."

To a second childless woman came the promise, "You will bear a child if you contribute a hundred dollars for the repair of the war god's temple in your village." Eager to carry out Kuan Yin's behest as mediated by the all-powerful priest, both women hurried home to share the verdict with their husbands.

Sometimes a healthy girl, praying for her invalid mother, would receive the temple priest's injunction, "*Ko Kan Chiu*

Mu—Cut liver, save mother." Twice during our earlier years in Changsha we had word of a courageous, devoted daughter who responded unhesitatingly, cut open her own abdomen with a huge knife, managed to snip off a bit of her liver, and had the piece cooked in a broth for her failing mother. "The gods have spoken. I must do their bidding and serve my mother, even though it costs me my life!"

One day, in a Buddhist temple high on the peak of a hill overlooking the river, I watched a worshiper who stood in front of the central altar. He was tall, clad in a simple gray gown, lost in meditation. The priest standing near by told me that he was one of the city's leading bankers. Three times a week after office hours, he climbed up to the temple for prayer and meditation, and stood there without moving for at least half an hour.

I continued to watch him at prayer, and noticed high above his head over the altar one of those lacquered tribute panels that are so frequently hung in temples as votive offerings. This one bore a striking inscription: "*Mo Tao Yu Ying*—Silent secret prayer receives response."

The worshiper believed devoutly in the words inscribed there. A few days later, I learned that his prayers were being offered in behalf of the father who was lying at death's door.

We came increasingly to think of those Changsha temples, beautiful in form, dark with a dim, religious light, as centers where the priests mediated between man and the unseen world. In the whole approach to disease the people believed there was no more potent force.

☯

Pilgrimages. Week after week, especially during the seventh and eighth months, long lines of pilgrims passed through

Changsha on their way south to Nan Yo, the Southern Sacred Peak, down in the Hengshan ranges. When a father in Chang-teh was mortally ill, the son vowed to undertake the pilgrim-age, and organized a little band to make the sacred journey with him. A woman in the west of the province, whose only son had an incurably enlarged head, heard the priest's verdict at the temple in Taoyüan and started on the long trek. Two sons took the vow to walk to Nan Yo, hoping their mother's tumor would thereby be made to disappear. Convinced as any who journeyed to Lourdes in later years that a holy pilgrimage would bring an answer to prayer for healing, several would find a way to journey together. Long lines of them would meet at some inn by the way and continue their march southward in a well-knit company. Their devout attitude, their singleness of purpose, made those yearly lines of pilgrims something we could never forget.

In the dispensary one day we heard over the wall the singing of pilgrims chanting their pilgrimage hymns. A reverent hush quieted the crowd in our waiting room, old men, young mothers, little children. We found ourselves humming the melody as we went about our work.

A SONG OF ASCENTS

> I come, with sincere and pious heart
>   and mind,
> To visit Nan Yo, the great, merciful,
>   and venerable.
> On the nine-dragon mount is manifest
>   the power of the gods
> Who meet together on the spiritual hill,
>   honored by the world.

On the bench beside the wall a child turned to his mother, questioning. She explained the singing to him, and told him of the power of the southern mountain. She reminded him, too, of the T'ai Shan stone seen on every street. Every child knew its meaning, knew that T'ai Shan, the Great Northern Mountain, was the most revered of all the sacred shrines.

As I listened, I recalled my own visit to Nan Yo, climbing the mountain by the stone road worn smooth and slippery by countless feet. I thought of the old woman with bound feet who refused to be carried up or down the sacred hill, and of the thanksgiving songs I had heard the pilgrims chanting.

As the pilgrims made their way down the main street of Changsha, we always watched them with respect. Each one wore the pilgrim's garb. On his blouse was sewn a white square on which were four large characters: *"Nan Yo Chin Hsiang—* To Nan Yo Mountain to Enter with Incense." It was a journey for worship.

They were an impressive company, walking always in single file, without haste, without lagging. Some groups made their pilgrimage more difficult of performance by vowing to stop at every seventh or ninth pace of the journey—often a couple of hundred miles—to kneel down, set on the ground before them their little shelf of incense sticks, and kotow, touching their heads to the ground in worship. Then they were off again with buoyancy, chanting as they renewed their steady march. It was as if we were watching the processions of many lands and many centuries. There had always been singing bands of pilgrims moving worshipfully toward a determined goal.

A modern-trained physician told me that when he was but five years old he had a very severe illness. His mother had gone to worship at the great city temple in Siangtan, the home of his boyhood, about thirty miles upriver from Changsha. After she had made her offering and prostrated herself, the priest told her that she ought to make the pilgrimage to Nan Yo to pray for the child's recovery. She made the vow at once. "If Ping-yang recovers, I will make the ascent of the sacred mountain, to the shrine on the very topmost peak."

"Mother took my two older sisters along as fellow pilgrims," the doctor said. "All three of them wore the pilgrim's garb as they made the journey, seventy-five miles to Nan Yo and back. It was not long before I recovered completely."

Some of the pilgrims went to pray for the souls of parents who had died. Priests provided them with sheets of printed prayers. One of the prayers read:

> We weep when our thoughts turn to the loved father we have lost. We implore you, Compassionate Ti-Tsang, to fling open the gates and lighten the gloom of hell for him. Lead him out from the place of pain, and grant him happiness.

Some of the pilgrims carried votive offerings: a new bell to be hung under the temple roof at home, a figure of the arm or leg that had been restored. All went in confidence and gratitude. More often than not those they passed would secretly determine to make a similar vow. Next year or the year after, perhaps, they, too, would make the long journey to the holy mountain. Hunan province was very proud of this famous peak, one of the Five Sacred Peaks of China. No one argued about their ancient power, their abiding influence. On the pages of early Chinese history everyone might read of the solemn pilgrimage of the Emperor Shun, over four thousand years before. He was celebrating, even then, an old liturgy of mountain worship that had already become established as a part of the religious inheritance of the race.

As they returned from Nan Yo, the pilgrims invariably walked with a buoyant gait, as if some mysterious miracle had been worked within them. Some brought back trophies—protective charms and amulets that would keep away demons and

harmful spirits. All were sure their prayers had been answered.
Every shrine they had passed on the mountainside was adorned
with lacquered votive panels, bearing an inscription of assurance:

> If there is prayer
> There is bound to be response.

The world of spirits! We could never fail to be conscious of
them. Everybody knew they were there, good and evil, dis-
pensers of favor, withholders of well-being, surrounding us by
day and by night. Mediators were needed by all human beings
to intercede with the more powerful good spirits to banish the
malignant, threatening ones. The mother was a mediator, calling the child's lost soul home. The apprentice, with his sticks
of incense, was fortifying the household against the spirits of
darkness. The priest with tinkling bells and cymbals, droning
his prayers for a good fee, was there to call for deliverance from
the spirits of disease. The temples and the pilgrimages were
ways of communication. It was these that must be depended
on, as a last resort, for contact with the world of spirits.

XXVI

GOOD COMPANIONS

住要好鄰　行要好伴

On a journey you need good companions;
At home you need good neighbors.

ON MY medical journeys in various provinces, often in sedan chairs, over difficult lonely country roads or in tiny boats that were rowed or poled when the wind failed, I learned much about the people.

The Robber Chief. Lu was the head of a guild of robbers. He had rescued an American doctor whom I knew years before when, during the Boxer year, his life was threatened. The county magistrate was a friend of the doctor's and gave him shelter in the yamen for a few nights. Finally, sitting together at breakfast one morning, he told the doctor that he was going to ignore the edict of the Empress Dowager to put all

Westerners to death in his area. He had devised a plan to send
his friend away to safety under an escort. He sent for Lu, the
robber chief, who came in trembling and kotowed before the
official, expecting to hear that he was to be executed for a
bandit raid of an earlier week.

Instead, the official told Lu to take the American doctor
across the county boundary and over into the next province
where things were quiet and he would be safe. Everybody knew
Lu. The magistrate said he would hold the bandit responsible
for the doctor's safety.

They passed through village after village where scowling
peasants and farmers seemed ready to threaten the life of the
guest. At each point, however, a word from the bandit chieftain scattered the crowd.

On one medical journey in the province of Kiangsi I stopped
for a meal at a lonely inn between the headwaters of two
rivers. I was sure I recognized my neighbor. "Weren't you the
man who helped the American doctor escape from Ch'aling
when his life was threatened several years ago? And didn't you
come to our hospital last year with Huang, the bandit who was
shot in the leg?"

"You did well to recognize me, sir. I have withdrawn from
the guild of robbers. Everyone knows me now as an honest
citizen."

"I know all about you," I told him. As we were alone in a
corner of the inn, I asked him a few questions about the robber's trade. "Does a robber," I inquired, "have a code of
morals?"

"Oh, yes. Did you never read about the robber's code in
the story told by Chuangtzŭ, the ancient philosopher?"

In Chuangtzŭ's anecdote a robber chief pointed out how
impossible it would be for a robber to achieve anything without morals. "By intuition he recognizes where something is

hidden—that is his greatness; he must be the first to get it
—that is his courage; he must be the last to get out—that is his
sense of duty; he must know whether it can be managed or
not—that is his wisdom; he must divide fairly—that is his
kindness."

No one, my companion pointed out, who is lacking in one
of these five virtues will ever become a great robber.

☯

The Laodah. "Have you always lived on this boat?" I asked
the laodah during another trip upriver in a tiny sailboat.

Yes, he replied. He was born on a boat very much like this
one. When his mother's time came, his father tied up to the
bank at a village he knew and sent for an old midwife who
came on board and took charge. The laodah was the first child,
so there was great rejoicing aboard. Even the villagers gave a
feast to the father and congratulated him, saying, "Now you
have a son who will grow up to be a laodah also." It was an old
saying: "Water always drops from the eaves into the same old
hole."

This particular laodah had a warm feeling toward the medical profession. Often he had taken an eminent doctor of the
old school out from Changsha and up the winding Liuyang
River to see the landlord of an old farm. He had taken the
doctor's prescription to the druggist's shop in a near-by town
and had searched here and there until he assembled all the in-
gredients for which it called. More than once he had stopped
at a village with his own wife and called for the village *p'o-p'o*
when a child was to be born.

I asked the laodah to tell me about the way in which injuries were treated in eastern Hunan, and about illnesses for
which he knew the cure. He said that in this part of the prov-

ince, Liuyang, a great many vegetable drugs were used. The practitioners often prescribed plasters that were black and forbidding, but potent in relieving pain. According to the laodah, they even drew out the roots of a patient's trouble.

I knew a good deal about the black plasters of Liuyang. Each doctor had his own special formula, and each shop preferred its own special design, round or square or diamond-shaped. I had seen hundreds of these counterirritant plasters applied and knew that everyone trusted them.

The laodah told me also of times when he had given safe escort to men who were outlaws from justice, trying to escape from the magistrate who offered a reward for their capture. I asked him where he had hidden them. He lifted up a board on the deck and showed me the shallow hold filled with straw, cabbages, and herb remedies. "Down there," he said, "anyone can hide safely. The freight is carried in that end of the hold, and where you are there is a little cabin for passengers."

The wind was constantly shifting and we had to do a great deal of poling as we went through the shallow stretches. In the evening, after we had stopped in one of the little villages to buy eggs and rice for the next day's meals, the laodah stopped and burned a few sticks of incense to ward off the evil spirits of the night, then uttered a long, low, moaning call. It sounded almost as if he were echoing the wind. He had uttered that call for so many years that he seemed to have caught the tone and quality of the breeze he needed. Within an hour, the wind began to blow softly and moved our boat.

As we glided along, the laodah said he was glad to be taking me up to Anyüan and asked if it was true that our hospital had proposed a plan to cure the miners at the collieries of a "stomach ailment."

I told the laodah about hookworm disease and how it was

recognized and treated. That river pilot, although his boat was small and his experience limited, was an understanding companion.

❂

The Innkeeper. We reached the outskirts of Yiyang late in the afternoon. It would soon be dark, and the chair bearers said we couldn't possibly reach the next town by daylight. The head chair bearer set me down in front of *Shun Fêng,* the Inn of the Favoring Wind, which, he said, was the best inn out here. Boatmen off that little river often stayed in it. If I wanted to go into the town of Yiyang, I might find a larger place, but he thought I would like this better.

Room and beds were always ready in one of these roadside establishments and as clean as could be expected out in the country. No traveler in America ever entered a hotel where rooms were so simply furnished: nothing but a wooden bedstead with wooden slats, a plain square wooden table, and a single chair. In the corner was a small wooden stand with a shining brass basin on top. The servant brought hot water for washing. Of course I had brought along my own *pei-wo*—no innkeeper ever furnished bedding for his guests.

Just before dark they served me a hot meal in my own room. There was rice, of course, all I wanted of it, and four bowls in the center of the table from which I could take what I desired: sweet and sour pork, an egg omelette, a dish of Chinese cabbage, cooked with bean sprouts, and another vegetable dish, steaming hot, all flavored to the most exacting traveler's taste. I was soon refreshed.

The landlord came out and sat down beside me for a chat over the teacups.

"You are having good rice crops this year," I began, for this part of Hunan province was famous for its rice, much of which was shipped down through Tungting Lake.

After he had commented about the recent abundant years, free from floods and drought, he asked me if I wasn't from the Hsiangya Hospital.

"You operated on my neck when I had a carbuncle," he told me. "The scar you made is still there and I often tell my friends about it. My name is Li Ping-chen. My brother was Li Ping-wu. When he had that big tumor in his shoulder we were always grateful to you for sending him to Hankow for treatment at the hospital near the Temple of the Military God."

He knew that we had moved up after the earlier years in Changsha to a place near the Gate of the Grass Tide, and that our medical teaching program began there. Many of our students had stopped at the inn on their way to Changsha.

"Do you remember Li Tsêh-ming, a short man who came from north of here up in the lake district?" he asked. "He always stopped here. After he became a doctor, he used to tell me to bring patients in, and we had a little dispensary downstairs in the front room."

The old innkeeper spoke, too, of former Premier Hsiung, whose home was out in the west of Hunan. On one occasion, while returning from Changsha, where he had attended the ceremony when we laid the cornerstone of one of our dormitories, Mr. Hsiung had told him that we had established a co-operative society to promote medical education. "Mr. Hsiung believed in your work thoroughly," he said. Then, as if it were an afterthought, "Wouldn't you like to treat a few sick persons tonight? They would be grateful and I am sure it would build up your constituency in Yiyang."

I agreed, of course, and saw about twenty patients, examin-

Pilgrims on Their Way to Nan Yo

The Hospital Ricksha
Man

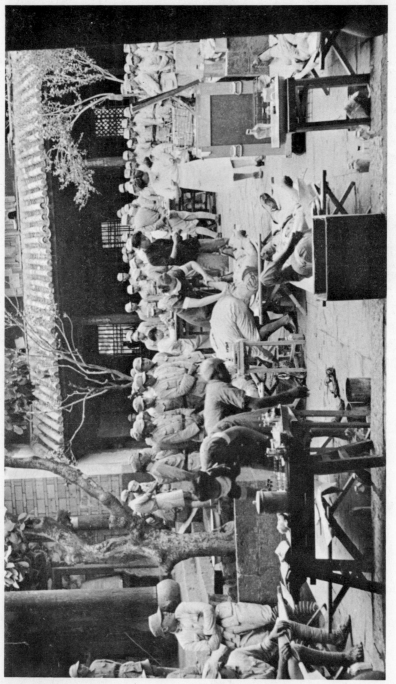

The Hsiangya Unit at the Fighting Front

ing them by the light of a kerosene lamp. One of them was the innkeeper's infant son, six months old, who had an eruption on his face and body. Another was a slave girl who had an abscess on the sole of her foot caused by a splinter that had run into it while she was out hunting for firewood. The old mother-in-law who was visiting her daughter came, too. Her pulse was very rapid and she needed digitalis.

When the chair bearers came round early the next morning, to take me on the next lap of the journey, I went to settle up.

"There is no charge for you, sir, either for room or for meals," the innkeeper said. "You have been our doctor and friend."

The County Magistrate. The Blue Express set me down at Suhsien station late one afternoon. That night at the doctor's house we planned the medical visits for the following day.

Suhsien was a wheat-growing district some distance north of the valley of the Long River, where rice was the principal crop. The great curse of this area was kala azar, a serious parasitic disease, fatal if not checked early and particularly cruel to children. When I went through the hospital, half the patients they showed me had kala azar.

In the afternoon we called on Mr. Wang, the county magistrate of Suhsien, and found him keen to know what preventive medicine could do for the region. "Let me come down and call on you at the hospital tomorrow," he suggested. "Then the hospital doctor and I can get your advice and can plan together for the county. I have read that China needs not only medicine to cure disease, but study to find the sources of disease and stamp them out."

Promptly at ten o'clock the next morning Magistrate Wang

arrived. We went through the hospital together, inspecting every ward, the laboratory, pharmacy, and the classrooms for the nurses. Out in the garden two boys were standing, one about six, the other fourteen years old. The magistrate questioned them. "From what village do you come?"

"From Hsi Hsiang, up in the hills, thirty li away."

"How many are there in your family?"

"Father and Mother and six children. We are two of the six."

"How many of you have this disease?"

I could see that a huge gap in the little boy's face had been left as one of the ravages of the dreaded kala azar.

"All eight of us have it, sir!" the older boy replied.

"Then why are only two of you here for treatment?"

The boy answered that his family had asked about the price of the medicine and had found that it was too costly for all of them. The wheat crop was only moderately good that year, and they couldn't afford to pay for treatment for all eight. The boys wanted to come because their friends in the next village had come and got completely well. "So we drew lots to see which two should come. The lots fell to us."

Magistrate Wang was deeply moved by this straightforward story. He insisted that a search be made in the villages throughout the county where kala azar existed. "If we have a record of all the houses in each village in the county, perhaps we can find ways to drive out this pestilence."

There was a man, I thought as I took the train back to Shanghai, who had already enlisted in the fight for health.

○

The Ferryboat Passenger. One day there came a hurry call to visit the county magistrate of Hsiangtan. Three chair bearers carried me south on the east bank of the river till we came to the main ferry where, chair and all, we went on board for the crossing.

As we were on the ferry, I asked the passenger at my side, "What is your honorable name?" He looked startled, something wholly unusual for a Chinese, and replied, "My name is Li."

We went on with the conversation about the weather and the rice crops. Presently, as we scrambled out of the ferryboat and up on the bank, my friend turned to me and apologized. "My name is really Ch'ên, not Li. You know, there is a Chinese word *ch'ên* which means 'to drown' and I couldn't think of uttering that word in a boat in the middle of a river. It would be too ominous."

I was always amazed at the power of words over Chinese emotions.

☯

The Nanping Health Officer. On another river journey, I was visiting the hospitals up the Min River in Fukien province, one of the most beautiful streams in China. We were on a huge houseboat towed by a steam launch and I began to wonder what would happen on that crowded craft if fire should break out. I had my medical bag with me, for one never knew when a consultation would be called for. At a turn in the river my colleague pointed out two beautiful pagodas, one on each bank of the river, emerging like spires from the groves of dark camphor trees that lined the banks. "Remember those pagodas," he said, "when we reach Nanping." We could already see the city in the distance.

The next day I stood at the boat landing of Nanping, where two great branches converged to form the main stream of the

Min River. I had just met the health officer of the county, and he was taking me to visit the city vaccination center.

"Many years ago," my companion told me, "a dreadful flood threatened this city. Both branches of the river were in spate and the entire lower part of the city was threatened. A soothsayer suggested the way out."

It is an ancient Chinese belief that fire is stronger than water and, as the soothsayer told them, a way would have to be found by which the symbol of fire could be made evident and cause the water to recede. He suggested that two pagodas be built, one on each bank of the main stream a mile down the river, and pointed out that, together with the inverted Y of the river, they would form the character for fire. The citizens erected the two pagodas, and the water subsided. "Nanping," the doctor assured me, "has never been flooded since."

XXVII
RESTLESS DECADE

古者以天

下為主君

為客

In ancient days the people were the host;
The ruler was the guest.

FOR three years after the death of the old Empress Dowager
Tz'ŭ Hsi, Yüan Shih-k'ai, her confidant, remained in seclusion. Whenever the Prince Regent sent for him, he made the
excuse that his lame leg would prevent effective service at court.
However, as soon as the revolution dethroned the Manchus,
Yüan became the leader of the counter-revolutionary clique
and forced his own election to the presidency. He determined
to have each provincial governorship held by one of his own
party, a man with a military background upon whom he could
depend to be ruthless in carrying out his instructions. In every
case he sent to a province as its commander in chief a man
from another province. Favorite sons could not be depended
upon if the province rebelled against the president.

One of the first political casualties of these restless years was our beloved governor T'an Yen-k'ai, who had been a friend even before we moved to the Street of the Grass Tide. His interest in the hospital dated from an attack of pneumonia in 1912 when Dr. Yen had attended him. For the first time in the annals of his family he had been treated with Western medicine only, and he was so completely won over to modern science that he persuaded the gentry to agree to the proposal that the province sign an agreement with the Yale University Mission for the starting of modern medical education.

T'an was proud that the new hospital and medical school had been built during his two terms as governor. Under his leadership the Hsiangya medical program forged ahead. He discovered, for example, that we could never do the kind of modern X-ray work required of our hospital, or much of the other scientific experimentation planned for our laboratories, without an adequate supply of electricity. Dr. Yen told him that our electric equipment had arrived two years earlier, but since there was no current it would have to lie unused in the storeroom.

So Governor T'an pushed forward a plan for the new power plant outside the North Gate, which would provide illumination and power for the hospital and laboratories as well as the faculty residences. One night in February of 1917, as we peered through the blackness, the whole hospital was suddenly lit up. It was like a symbol of the goal toward which we had been pressing for a dozen years.

The governor was equally interested in our laboratories, although the experimental approach to medicine was entirely new to him. When we heard that he was coming to inspect the anatomy laboratory for the first time, we were discouraged. We hadn't a single cadaver there. The northern and southern armies were fighting outside the city gates. The governor was to make the visit on Monday. On Sunday morning, while the northern armies were hurriedly evacuating the barracks to the east of Changsha, the anatomy teacher and I decided to get our own supplies.

As the Kwangsi troops poured in through the South Gate and mopped up remnants of the enemy in the city streets, I asked the governor to send along two squads of soldiers to accompany us on our search. I went with one squad into the center of town, while the anatomy teacher went out through the north suburb.

At about six o'clock that Sunday afternoon there was great excitement in the dormitory. Word was passed around that we were returning with several loads of "laboratory material."

All that night the student body worked with the anatomy teacher to finish the storage tanks. Fortunately they had all the carbolic acid and other chemicals needed to preserve the material. By daylight on Monday it was all put away, and the new anatomy building was ready for the inspection of its beloved patron.

When the governor visited the new laboratory, he went inside hesitantly, grasping his nose as if afraid of some airborne infection. The odor of the powerful disinfectants was strange to him, but he went through the experience bravely. As he came out and saw the entire student body gathered round, he greeted them with a smile and said, "You are to be congratulated. You are the first students in the whole of Central China to have anatomical dissection made available to you. Tell the people about it. Take them in to see the laboratory for themselves. Explain to them how essential dissecting is for those who are to be modern physicians."

T'an was a stanch foe of the reactionaries. President Yüan had removed him from his first term of office and had replaced him with an official who made the whole province rebellious. We all knew that his removal from office a second time would mean grave personal danger to Governor T'an.

I was not entirely surprised when Mr. Nieh appeared at my office one evening just before dark. "Are you free to go with me on an important matter?" he asked. I had planned to walk down to the river with the children. We always loved to go out through the Gate of the Grass Tide and stand at the edge of the embankment, looking across to the glow of a flaming sunset. But when I saw the expression of anxiety on Mr. Nieh's face, I asked him what he would like me to do.

"Could you go out with your children some other time, and come with me now?"

A Chinese gentleman of breeding would never have made such an insistent request unless he were deeply troubled about something, so I sent the children back to the house without delay, and started out through the hospital gate with Mr. Nieh.

As we hurried along, we spoke of the ceaseless warfare in Central China during the previous nine months. Hunan province had been a battleground as always. Our hospital was overflowing with soldiers injured at the front or sick with dysentery and malaria.

After about fifteen minutes of rapid walking, we came to a great mansion in the northeast quarter of the city. The gatekeeper must have known about Mr. Nieh's errand and spied him through the little window at the side, for the gates seemed to fly open. We were shown through courtyards and corridors to a magnificent reception room. Mr. Nieh led the way in. We found ourselves in the center of a group of eight of the most prominent of the Changsha gentry—bankers, merchants, literati. Most of them were on the board of our hospital and medical college; all were friends of many years' standing.

We bowed to each other as friends do in China, sat down and began to sip fragrant hot tea. Not a word was said for three or four minutes. Then, one after another, four brief sentences.

"Fu Liang-tso is coming here tomorrow to take over the governorship of Hunan." It was Mr. Shên, long recognized as the senior statesman of Changsha, who broke the silence.

"Doctor Hume, there will be no steamer for Hankow till Saturday night." This time the speaker was Mr. Ts'ao, the chairman of our medical college board.

I began to see light. The coming of the reactionary Fu would unquestionably mean danger to T'an and all his group.

Another long pause, then I was the third to speak. "Send him to my house at daybreak tomorrow." I knew he would be safe in our home. Others had taken refuge there before.

One could feel an immediate sense of relief in the room. The group started to break up. Mr. Shên spoke once more. "Mr. Yang will be at your house by six o'clock tomorrow morning." No one had mentioned the name of T'an.

Mr. Nieh and I bowed and took our leave. As we walked back to the hospital through the now dark streets, neither of us said a word. I was too busy putting together the pieces of the picture puzzle in which those four sentences were the fragments. A new governor was at hand. The Changsha gentry had hoped the foreign doctor would offer refuge to their beloved citizen until he could be sent away safely on the Saturday-night steamer. The doctor had proposed the very thing they wanted. A fictitious name had been devised for Governor T'an. Would everything work out as planned?

At the hospital gate Mr. Nieh bade me a friendly good night, and added, "Be sure to speak of him as Mr. Yang. His life will be in great danger until he reaches Hankow."

Early the next morning, T'sai Sz-fu woke me with a knock on the door. "There is a Mr. Yang downstairs who says he would like to see you."

I hurried down to find our distinguished refugee in the

plainest of peasant garb. He had arrived in a rough, country sedan chair, its long bamboo poles borne by but two carriers. As governor, he was accustomed to a state sedan chair with at least four carriers, with runners before and behind. I showed him to his room upstairs and arranged for his meals to be served there. If he came to the dining room on the ground floor, someone might drop in and recognize him.

Those were memorable days with Governor T'an in our home. We talked about medical education and politics, about religion and the life of the people. He told me many things about his father, who had been a viceroy and who had left to his son a legacy of classical scholarship. Starting with the local provincial tests, he had gone up, by stages, to take the national examination in Peking. Eventually he had captured top honors in the examination of the Hanlin Academy, which equipped him for the highest political appointments.

One evening he talked to me for hours about his democratic ideals. Though his father had hoped he would become a high official, the son was sure before he was thirty that China deserved something better than an imperial monarchy. He had mastered the teachings of Rousseau and Lincoln even before the year of the Boxer movement when the Empress Dowager fled to Sian. He knew the Manchu Dynasty was doomed, and wondered what political leadership the younger men in Hunan should follow.

"What finally led you to side with the young revolutionaries?" I inquired.

That grew out of a fortunate meeting with Sun Yat-sen, he said. T'an had met Sun after the doctor's return from England, where he had been confined in the Chinese embassy by the Manchus who hated and feared him. Dr. Cantlie, one of his medical teachers at Hong Kong, brought pressure through the British Government and obtained his release. After meeting Sun, T'an determined to follow in his footsteps and work to make China a "people's nation."

We talked of the years just before 1911 when I had first met him at the monthly sessions of the *Wên Hsüeh Hui*, the Association for Literary Studies. The restaurant where we gathered was a famous old rendezvous for political schemers. "You foreigners hadn't known that these gatherings included only the radicals of the province. After the Western guests went home, the others stayed on to plan for the great day of liberation." They had welcomed us because our presence did much to allay official suspicion.

As he told me the remarkable story of those final years before 1911 when the sands of the Manchu Dynasty were running out so rapidly, I was more than ever grateful that T'an had become our friend. I persuaded him to write several Chinese couplets for me in his large bold hand. He spent a little time trying to teach my son how to hold the Chinese penbrush, but most of his day was spent in writing epigrams and matched phrases to be mounted on scrolls, or in composing personal letters.

A few trusted friends, warned to ask at the door for Mr. Yang, came to call, but even they were timid. The spies of the new governor were everywhere and we did not want them to discover that the Yali campus was a meeting place for political agitators. Dr. Yen met each day with the influential members of the gentry, and brought their messages to our house in person. The campus gateman kept careful watch for unrecognized strangers.

Saturday evening, warning came of danger, and about nine o'clock we escorted "Mr. Yang" to the riverbank under cover of darkness. We had borrowed the British-American Tobacco Company's launch and it was to wait for us at the steps near the northwest corner of the city wall. One of the Yali campus night watchmen walked along, lighting our way with a paper lantern bearing a large red Chinese character *Yang*, the assumed name of our guest.

The current in the river was strong that night. Our friend grew increasingly nervous because the launch made headway so slowly. He said several times that the new governor's scouts were out searching for him. They were likely, he feared, to be soldiers from a northern province; no native of Hunan would ever betray Governor T'an. We had gone but half a mile upstream when a volley of shots rang out suddenly, as if they had been fired directly above us.

We suggested to the laodah that he steer a course farther away from the bank, just along the outer edge of a row of cargo junks. We moved against that racing flood as noiselessly as we could, but Governor T'an told me afterward that he could hear his own heartbeat above the rush of the water.

Finally, after fighting the current for two long miles, we reached the steamer landing and made fast to the outer side of the ship, away from the wharf. The darkness on that side gave us a chance to get on board without detection, and we made our way to a cabin on the upper deck, reserved for "Mr. Yang."

Our guest had begged me to travel with him to Hankow, but the work of the hospital was too pressing for me to leave. I sent one of our short-term American teachers along to stay by him in the British concessions in Hankow until he was on board a British steamer bound for Shanghai.

Just before saying good night, I had a personal word with Governor T'an. "My friend, you will be back here before long. The province of Hunan depends on you to lead it. We all look for your early return. All of us in the Hsiangya Hospital think of you as our founder and patron."

Tsai hui!—We shall meet again!

On Monday morning a telegram came in saying that Governor T'an had reached Hankow without incident. After reaching Shanghai, a few days later, he abandoned the alias, Mr. Yang. Before long, he sent each of us a pair of handsome scrolls with personally written sentences of gratitude.

XXVIII

CRUSADING FOR HEALTH

窮人無病
抵半富

A poor man without illness is half a rich man.

ONE of the governors that President Yüan imposed upon
Hunan during those turbulent years was, we had reason to
hope, a liberal, a man with a scientific point of view who would
understand our medical situation and aid in our health program. We found Governor T'ang a suave, well-bred man who
had traveled widely and spoke fluent French, had taken his
naval training in France and was familiar with European ways.
The Yale University Mission group invited the new governor
to a formal luncheon on the day after he took office in Changsha. Our colleague, Dr. Yen, was master of ceremonies. He had
already been sent for as medical consultant and had become a
favorite of the official retinue at the yamen. Three Hunan cabinet members were present, the commissioner of finance, the

commissioner of civil affairs, and the commissioner of education. Some of the heads of leading government schools were also present.

There were the usual speeches of welcome and the usual photographs. The new governor responded graciously, but gave no hint of the platform President Yüan had outlined. After luncheon everyone withdrew to the garden, and the Westerners present, wholly unsuspecting, thought they had led off with a good show.

The following day we had bad news about three of our luncheon guests. That noon, in a public square near the yamen, the treasurer of the province was publicly shot, while the other two senior cabinet members, the commissioners of civil affairs and of education, were thrown into a common prison, sentenced to be executed within two days.

The atmosphere was tense. The leading gentry and the students in all the city schools were stirred as seldom before. It was hard to keep schools going, but word was received by every principal that guards were being placed at the front gates to prevent pupils from leaving for student-union meetings. "Any principal," the governor's proclamation read, "permitting students to hold political assemblies on school grounds will be dismissed. If he is a foreigner, his embassy will be requested to repatriate him."

The treasurer was dead. We discussed anxiously what we could do to save the lives of our other two good friends, both of whom had been working with us to strengthen the board of the newly launched medical college, and to secure the government subsidies that we had been promised.

Dr. Yen hurried to the yamen and brought personal pressure on the governor. I got a sampan and rushed across the river to the British consul to get his co-operation. We went down, every couple of hours, to the central public square to make inquiries. On one of these trips, two volleys rang out just as Dr. Yen and I entered the square. Bystanders told us that executions had been going on there steadily ever since daybreak. They had just shot two more officials. People thought they were the commissioner of civil affairs and the commissioner of education.

Greatly discouraged, Dr. Yen and I called on the governor together. We learned that the two commissioners were still alive. The governor was trying to decide whether their lives might be spared. In a sense, he was not a free agent. Though there was no accusation against them, no suggestion that they had been traitors, Peking insisted that they were among the three top officials of the province and that the only way to teach Hunan the lesson of subservience to the president was to execute all three. There could be no room in imperial China for any officials who were in sympathy with Sun Yat-sen, men such as T'an or Huang or Ts'ai of Hunan. There was much urgent argument, during which it became evident that the governor didn't want to lose Dr. Yen as his personal medical consultant. Further, he knew how valuable an intermediary Dr. Yen might prove if negotiations should be necessary with any of the foreign consuls. He finally consented to let the sentence be commuted from "death at dawn tomorrow" to life imprisonment.

The succeeding years of Governor T'ang's term became increasingly a reign of terror. Although he supported our medical work and paid over the provincial subsidies with fair regularity, we were unhappy that the Hsiangya item in the Hunan budget increased the burden of taxation on the farmers. They were told that the increase was due to "the insistence of the foreigners."

Gradually the provincial gentry realized that the governor was merely the ruthless agent of the hated Yüan. They did all they could to support Ts'ai, the fearless Hunan leader who was now engineering the revolt against Yüan.

After Yüan's death in 1916, Governor T"ang was one of the early political casualties. At the end of June, 1916, he fled for his life. Dressed as a peasant he escaped through the East Gate. As he hurried along by the rice fields and vegetable gardens, he passed the gateway of the Hsiangya Hospital where he had visited us often. He would have been glad to take refuge there, but his trusties hurried him along.

For a day and a night the party walked, hiding in way-side temples when they heard the sound of marching feet. One of T"ang's men who had been a barber shaved off the general's mustache to improve his disguise. Early the second morning they managed to put the refugee on board a British river steamer that was passing Siangyin. He was not detected in the melee of passengers that climbed on the ship and, eventually, he reached Shanghai safely. His political career was over.

Some years later while riding in a Shanghai bus, I found myself seated beside a dignified Chinese gentleman in a long silk gown. His hair was turning gray and he wore very dark glasses, possibly to shield himself from the gaze of the inquisitive. Something made me recognize that my neighbor was former Governor T"ang. We greeted each other and I inquired what he was doing.

"I have retired," he replied, "and am giving myself up to the reading of the Buddhist scriptures."

With Yüan's death there broke loose a plague of war lords that tormented China for a decade. Those of Yüan's generals who were strong enough to build up independent armies hired mercenary soldiers. They became roving bands that wandered over the land and terrorized people everywhere, looting, raping, murdering.

In the hospital our work expanded in spite of the disorders, and although we tried to keep out of politics, it was sometimes almost impossible to avoid being involved. Many of the officials, who were powerful individuals one day and fugitives the next, had been outwardly friends of the Hsiangya movement.

Meanwhile we were wondering whether Dr. Sun Yat-sen would come forward now and seize the chance to give democracy a fresh start. Unhappily, he was still a fugitive, but he continued to gather loyal spirits about him at every center he could reach.

Sun had been educated as a doctor in Hong Kong and was filled with a deep concern for the people's social welfare. As he planned for the new China, he foresaw that there must be a national health program for the country. The people were too poor to provide for themselves a modern system of medical care. His influence, we discovered, was bringing about a new attitude among our dispensary patients. Their old fears and hesitancies about our hospital were disappearing. They begged for "rules of health," and we had to print many editions of simple instructions on How to Keep Well. Another leaflet we issued was Sun Yat-sen Wants China to Be Healthy.

Another crusader for health who became very influential in Changsha was Têng T'ai-t'ai, an aristocrat of the old school. Her feet were still bound, she had always dressed in silk, and had spent her life in a spacious mansion; but throughout most of her life she had never concerned herself with the well-being of the common people.

One day there came an opportunity for her to use her daring and aggressive mind. A bulletin fell into Têng T'ai-t'ai's hands describing the starting of our Social Service League for the women of Changsha. Although she was a thoroughly competent classical scholar, the words meant little to her. She had to call in her daughters-in-law and learn from them what the phrase "social service" meant.

As she read on, she learned of the contrast between Changsha and the modern cities of the Western world. Changsha, a city of three hundred thousand persons, had no sewers. The cities of the West took care of all that by well-planned systems laid out by sanitary engineers.

So Têng T'ai-t'ai hurried over to our home with two of her neighbors. What would the doctor and his wife suggest? When the houseboy brought in tea and cake, Têng T'ai-t'ai protested. "Let us not take time for formalities today. We have come to see you about approaching the governor of the province to lay out a system of sewers for the city of Changsha and to do it without delay."

Here, plainly, was a crusader who believed in action. She was so far ahead of the deliberateness and formality of conservative old China as to make it plain that she should lead our new Social Service League.

Wherever Têng T'ai-t'ai went during those next few weeks, whether she was talking with educators or religious workers or politicians, the one thing she insisted on was the civic responsibility of the women of Changsha. They must take the lead in giving the city a new health program.

She asked us to call with her on the police commissioner. She inquired bluntly what provisions there were in the city for sanitation and drainage. He told her that of course each compound in the city had one or more private wells. The overflow of these wells trickled out between bricks and clay into the tiny winding drains underneath the streets. She asked him to tell us how they kept the shallow drains clean.

He wasn't too well informed, but said that when a drain became blocked and overflowed, the shopkeepers along the street would complain and, finally, workmen would be sent to lift up the huge paving blocks stretching across the street. "They remove the obstruction," he added, "by poking at it with long bamboos."

"Is there no water supply," we asked him, "that can be tapped to flush these street drains?" He told us, with complete unconcern, that no such provision was needed in "a clean city like Changsha," although he admitted that some day, after the republic was really established, the central government might insist on a sanitary program for all the provincial capitals.

A few days later a British water-works engineer from Shanghai was visiting Changsha and we talked it all over with him. We told him of Têng T'ai-t'ai's enthusiasm, and took him out on a walk through some of the winding streets of the old city —streets that may well have been the pattern for some of the crooked lanes in old London.

We walked along West Long Street and up the hill to the Dyke by the Treasurer's Yamen, then on into still narrower lanes. Our own residence opened out into the Street of the Star of Long Life. The engineer smiled as we told him what the names meant. "I should think," he commented, "that Old Man Thunder, whose temple we are passing, would be tempted to persuade his goddess companion to let her lightning strike some of those mean landowners who refuse to spend money on public health." He pointed out that it was not a problem of drains only, but of fire hazards and ventilation as well. The Social Service League of Changsha had a heavy assignment ahead of it if it was going to bring about a health revolution in this old provincial capital.

We asked him what would be needed to set matters right so that the Hsiangya Hospital could work with these civic-minded women.

"To do a proper job, the whole city of Changsha will have to be razed to the ground and rebuilt completely," he answered. "This will include, of course, the provision of an adequate water supply. Têng T'ai-t'ai's goal is thoroughly sound, but it will require a far greater outlay of time and money than she now realizes."

But the Social Service League didn't have to wait. It found ready to hand a more tangible health technique, one that they could use at once. They determined to use the dramatic instinct of every Chinese man, woman, and child by putting on health shows.

In every public square, on Long River Street, in every temple courtyard, there were peep shows and Punch and Judy shows to be seen all the time, with old and young crowding round them. Every temple courtyard in China had a magnificent theatrical platform raised well above the ground so that the crowds might have a good view, especially during the chief festival seasons of the year, when people were accustomed to watching dramatizations of *The Dream of the Red Chamber*, stories from *The Romance of the Three Kingdoms*, and many other scenes from the pageant of China.

Dr. Peter of the Council on Health Education in Shanghai came to Changsha at our request, bringing a well-planned health demonstration. On the stage was a traveling belt with the erect figures of men moving steadily along. At the end of the belt was a big Chinese coffin. The display was so well timed that the lecturer could truthfully say, each time a man dropped over the brink into the coffin, "A death from tuberculosis has occurred somewhere in China."

Acting on the new enthusiasm, the Social Service League put in a public place a working model of a tuberculosis sanatorium with slots for coins. Before long the people of Changsha had contributed enough money to build a modern sanatorium for the city. The government donated an adequate plot of ground a little way north of our hospital.

Dr. Yen was really the moving spirit of the enterprise. He persuaded the leading men and women of the city to form an active committee, and he himself outlined a program that the citizens might develop. When the sanatorium was opened, there was hardly room for the patients who crowded to the doors.

Little by little the idea spread to other provincial capitals, and the fight against tuberculosis really got under way. The leaders regularly brought in students from all over Hunan to learn how to give the health message. Schoolboys, and girls also, went out into the countryside in bands. They taught the people how to transform a part of their own homes into sunlit platforms where, except in the most wintry weather, a tuberculosis patient might rest and regain his health. They developed a modification of the well-known Chinese "wind cap" so that the patients could be adequately protected even in inclement weather.

But it soon became evident that the magistrates and people of a couple of thousand counties in China could not be made aware of their health needs unless they were dealt with as a national issue. Fortunately, the offers of the health section of the League of Nations were welcomed in China. Acting on the advice of experts sent out by the League, a National Health Administration was established under the leadership of Dr. J. Heng Liu. Before long this led to a nation-wide program, centrally administered, with the provinces acting in accord with the national headquarters.

This national consciousness of the need of community health was not born overnight. It was remote from the days when we in Changsha lived in constant fear that the city might be destroyed by one or another of the war lords. During that time the loyalty of our Chinese friends was our strongest defense. Once, long after midnight, we heard the voice of Goliath calling to us. "Please move your beds back from the windows. There is a lot of shooting going on here."

A few minutes later we heard him shouting in his resonant voice, "Listen, you soldiers up on the city wall. Point your rifles the other way. This is the foreign doctor's house. Don't fire this way. These are our friends."

XXIX

SAVIORS OF THE CITY

To see what is right
And fail to do it
Is the mark of a coward.

DURING some of these chaotic years our medical enterprise went forward with scarcely an interruption. It was hard to convey to friends at a distance our sense of the continuity of our work. When news in the American press grew alarming, saying that Changsha was surrounded by fighting armies, we received cable inquiries.

"Yes," we replied promptly, "it is true that serious fighting is going on around our campus this week, but we go right on with our work, both medical and academic." We kept the students on the campus and treated in the dispensary those venturesome patients who came out to us through the Little

North Gate. The hospital basement repeatedly became a refugee center as well as a place for outpatients.

When the northern armies were thrown out of Changsha and a southern force marched in, the city streets were hung with flags and scrolls proclaiming a welcome to the newcomers. It was easier to welcome them than to turn that walled city into a shambles with street fighting. Perhaps the southern occupation would last six weeks before another northern force would march in from Hankow and Yochow, proclaiming that its commander was now the head of the government at Changsha. One winter there were ten different commanding generals at the head of the province. One or two of them held office for but a few days.

None of the governors brought along adequate medical advisers, so Dr. Yen and I were often summoned to the yamen. As doctors we found ourselves caught inextricably in the whirlpool of political change.

One day the telephone rang in my house. "This is the governor speaking. Are you Doctor Hume? Please come to the yamen at once. A division of the Kwangsi Army broke through the Hunan defenses southwest of Hengshan three days ago and is marching on Changsha. We must use every means to prevent fighting near the capital or on the east side of the river. You can help turn the tide."

Half an hour later, Mr. Warren of the Methodist Mission and I received detailed instructions in the governor's private office at the yamen. The room was evidently that of a military commander. There were sectional maps on the walls showing every road, all the contours, the terrain at every point. The position of attacking and defending troops was recorded on the maps every few hours. The governor was at least well informed. Whether he had a large enough force or sufficient military skill to turn back the ambitious army from Kwangsi remained to be seen. The southwestern general was again seeking control of Hunan province, this time not merely as a roving war lord but as a step toward the consolidation of his power throughout the whole south, from the sea to the Yangtze River.

"Today," the governor urged, "we count on you two esteemed foreign gentlemen, who have become citizens of Hunan like ourselves, to help in keeping these troublemakers away. Changsha must not become the scene of such bombardment as occurred during the bloody days of the revolution. I beg you to go to the front and plead with the Kwangsi commander to lead his troops across the river. If there is to be a battle, let it take place in the country, over there beyond Yolu Shan. You will be rendering lifesaving service to all Hunan. I beg you not to be afraid. You shall have all possible military protection."

We both spoke mandarin and were known by the citizens round Changsha, but the Kwangsi patrols would not recognize us. They were known to be antiforeign. We might be fired on. But we agreed to go.

As we started we felt not unlike the six citizens of Calais who knelt before the English king with halters round their necks as they pled with him to spare their city; or perhaps even more like Abraham when he interceded with Jehovah to spare Sodom, so soon to be bombarded by celestial explosives. We could have made out a better case than Abraham did, for there were many more than fifty righteous persons in Changsha!

It was a comical procession. My colleague, a massive Englishman, was mounted on a small, vicious, buff-colored Hunan pony that was full of energy. It was all the rider could do to control the restive creature. My pony was a drab dark-brown, his color matching his dull, listless nature. Behind us, in plain costume and with concealed pistols, hurried six of the governor's personal guard. Military uniforms might more easily draw the fire of the Kwangsi patrols. They carried white flags to use when they came in sight of the enemy troops.

Out we rode through the South Gate, on beyond the south suburb. There were very few people on the road, though ordinarily at this forenoon period the vegetable markets south of the city would have been jammed. Farther on, the highway was deserted, though it was broad daylight. It was as still as death.

Suddenly a shout, and we were surrounded, but not by Kwangsi soldiers. Two battalions of the governor's Hunan guard, who knew that we were out scouting, had been in ambush, hoping to take the advance patrols of the Kwangsi force by surprise.

"We frightened the Kwangsi men away!" they called out to us. "We drove them down to the riverbank. They commandeered all the boats down at the landing and are now rowing hard to get across to the west bank."

We asked how barely two hundred men could turn back a couple of thousand of the enemy's crack troops. An officer told us that his troops had instructed all the farmers going south to spread the report, when they met the Kwangsi advance guard, that the governor had suddenly received reinforcements; that five thousand fully armed troops were right behind them, and that these troops were being followed by a strong detachment of artillery. The farmers were frightened, but put so much conviction into their story that even before they reached the ambush many of the Kwangsi troops had straggled away. Just as they reached the Hunan battalion, it fell on them, firing repeated volleys and shouting as if it numbered a thousand men. The entire body of the two thousand Kwangsi men turned and fled.

Our mission was over. We rode back into the city at the

head of two battalions of Hunan soldiers. The governor presented us to a large group of citizens at a public reception, soon after, as the "saviors of the city"!

Into our modern hospital outside the North Gate, more and more military officers came to us. Some of them were really ill; others wanted a place of refuge. I was making rounds one day and went in to examine the patient in our most expensive private room. I had looked at the chart and was in the midst of questioning him when the door flew open and two messengers came to the side of the bed, saluted, and handed a telegram to the patient. He read it hurriedly, jumped out of bed where he had been lying under the covers in the uniform of a full general, put on his military raincoat, saluted me, and was gone. It was such a frequent occurrence during all those restless years that I had not even noticed, when I came into his room, that two sentries had been posted at the door. He had to be guarded day and night. The generals of the Hunan Army couldn't be too careful.

Not long after, Colonel Huang, another of our army friends, came to see me about his cough. "It is very disturbing at night," he told me. "I lose a lot of sleep. Can I come into the hospital for a week?"

I looked him over thoroughly and found little. I was sure he could stay at home and come to the clinic three times a week to have his throat painted.

"No!" he insisted. "Let me tell you why I want to come. My wife is the real patient. You have seen her dispensary record and have ordered that she be admitted, but she is very timid and hesitates to come in. She begged me the other day not to compel her to have the operation that you think necessary. Finally, my wife and I made a bargain. I felt this tickling in my throat and promised her I would exaggerate my complaint and get admitted to the hospital, too, so that I might have a private room on the men's side, while she had one across the building. She and I will both come in tomorrow if you give the word." I decided that his complaint justified letting him be hospitalized.

The friendship of these officials who were our patients was invaluable to us. Since we were, in reality, medical aides to the various generals, our senior medical staff was always informed as to the password, so that we could go in and out through the gates like protected beings. Dr. Yen and I were frequently at the yamen, at the barracks outside the East Gate, or at some emergency military headquarters just north or just south of the city. No one ever threatened us, no one attacked or injured us, but we always had to send a messenger to the governor to ask for the password. It would come to us sealed in a large official envelope. The password each night was in two syllables, but it was essential to know that there was a special secret by which any impostor might be trapped. Although there were two syllables, in replying only the first one must be given.

Those trips were a test of nerves. The narrow winding streets were tunnels of darkness into which our sedan chairs plunged. The faint glimmer of light from the oiled-paper lanterns that swung from the chair poles only seemed to intensify the blackness beyond its feeble ray. The tread of the bearers' straw sandals, usually so soft, seemed like the clanging of cymbals, while the flame of the lanterns was but a target toward which the muzzles of guns might be pointed.

Suddenly, out of the darkness would echo the call, "*K'ou Hao!*—Password!"

A brief tense moment! Would we forget the clue and give more than the single syllable? Had the muzzle of a gun not been pointing so directly at us, calling for the password might have been reassuring. Presently we would be jogging down another street, glad of an interval for more easy breathing. Again the *K'ou Hao!* summons would ring out. Finally, assured by each experience, we learned to give the password with confidence.

XXX
"YES, BUT . . ."

兵臨告急

必須死戰

Extreme peril requires violent effort.

DURING one night of terror for the patients in our wards I was
called three times to come and see first one then another of
the fires as the barracks east of the city blazed. The American
nurse went through the women's wards trying to reassure the
patients, now almost hysterical with fear. They knew what
to expect, for retreating armies always destroyed everything as
they fled, leaving villages in confusion and ruins. Only one
barracks remained, just to the east of our academic campus.
The northern army would surely seize those buildings if the
southern forces left them standing.

Within a stone's throw of our hospital stood the powder
magazine, a sinister neighbor capable of destroying our entire
community. The moat that circled it was the only external

evidence that it might be a storehouse of tons of gunpowder.

We made a plan. There was likely to be a short interval between the withdrawal of the southern army and the occupation of the city by the oncoming northern victors. This offered us a chance. With the help of Goliath, we determined to empty the powder magazine.

At dawn, I telephoned my proposal to Mr. Ts'ao, chairman of our Hsiangya medical board, who was now acting mayor of the city. He was delighted with the idea and said the city fathers would welcome our plan to get rid of that powder.

Promptly at eight o'clock I called up the American consul, gave him a hurried description of our imminent danger, and told him that the new hospital was sure to be terribly damaged if the magazine was blown up. I added that the city fathers had given us their approval.

He started to ask for more details, but I interrupted. "Tell me, sir, may I go ahead, take some men with me, force an entrance into the powder magazine, and dump the contents into the moat?"

There was a moment's hesitation before he spoke.

"Yes, but . . ."

I hung up the receiver so as not to hear any instructions that would limit our program. I was afraid the consul would remind me that the hospital was of reinforced concrete construction and that an explosion over at the magazine could only shatter our north windows. Consuls always have to advise moving cautiously.

I sent for the hospital engineer and told him to get his tools together; we might have to wreck the door of the powder magazine. It was heavily barricaded. Unless we could find the key we should have to use force. "Get Goliath and two helpers," I told him, "and meet me over there by the moat sharp at noon."

He checked his watch with mine and went off, relieved. It was he who had so often told me how serious an explosion over there would be for all our buildings.

The magazine was wholly unguarded as we came up to the moat. We looked for the gateman whose hut was over among the trees. Presently a shrinking little figure came out to meet our wrecking party.

"Let me have the key to the magazine," I ordered. He and I both knew that my authority was wholly fictitious.

"Oh, no, sir. I can't give it to you. The key is always kept in the office of the governor's bodyguard, down at the yamen in the city." He cringed as he spoke, as if he feared we would use force.

"I shall give you just twenty minutes to run down there and bring that key to me from the guardhouse. You will have to run both ways. If the key isn't back in that time, our engineer will force the gate open. Hurry!"

"Yes, sir, I'll run." He turned to go, but the sudden motion of his body caused a tiny clink. I seized him and tore his coat open. There was the huge key, hanging by a heavy chain around his neck. The man saw he was helpless. He really seemed grateful when he discovered that his responsibility for the explosives was ended.

The key was a narrow iron bar, fully a foot long, bent over at the end, and with numerous notches in its edge—not so secure from inquisitive thieves as the key of a Yale lock, but adequate for the protection of the powder magazine. We fitted the key into the ponderous lock, lifted it off, threw open the heavy barred door, and went inside. The walls were six feet thick, of solid brick and mortar. The air in the great chamber within was almost stifling for lack of ventilation. The floor was piled high with nearly three hundred tin containers that had once been used for retailing kerosene oil but were now packed solid with gunpowder. In the background were twenty rifles, each with a fixed bayonet, as well as a few cartridge belts. With the help of the men, we took the tins outside, pierced each several times with a bayonet, then systematically dropped them into the moat.

With each thud and splash, as the explosive was sucked under the water, the daring of our venture fascinated us. Before dark we had pitched fourteen tons of gunpowder into that moat. In the uncertain light of the rising moon we returned to the hospital, threading in single file between the rice fields. The pull of our muscles reminded us that each of the tins had weighed more than a hundred pounds.

I had hardly dropped off to sleep in the surgeon's dressing room of the hospital when Goliath brought in a messenger who had run twenty miles that day to warn the city that the approaching army belonged to Chang Ching-yao. I started up. We were in for a bad time. This General Chang belonged to the Anfu clique and was known as the most cruel and ruthless war lord in China. One of his officers, according to the messenger, was marching southward by another road to seize the city of Liling. Between them they would reduce Hunan province to a shambles unless the provincial armies were immediately turned over to them as well as all the provincial tax revenues.

I knew that I must act without delay to keep General Chang from filling the magazine with powder again. But how? The messenger had scarcely disappeared when a hospital orderly rushed in and shouted, "Come quickly to the hospital roof." A new fire had broken out to the east of the railroad line, and we could see the sky to the north lit up with a red glow. It looked as if the northern general was setting fire to villages that resisted him. He would surely reach the city not later than the next forenoon.

A few minutes later stretcher bearers started to come in with wounded and burned villagers from as far as ten miles to the north. They told ghastly stories of the cruelty of the northern soldiers. So many injured kept coming in that, presently, I sent out a team of our own orderlies and stretcher bearers with an intern to give first aid to the worst cases directly at the front. Before long, the operating rooms were filled with gunshot cases that needed prompt treatment, and the corridors were lined with other groaning patients. One of the junior surgeons took me aside and whispered, "There aren't beds enough in the hospital for the cases that have already come into the building. We must have more room and more beds at once."

Suddenly the idea flashed into my mind that we might convert the powder magazine into a hospital annex. Although it was midnight, I sent for my sedan chair and rushed into the city to consult a few of the leading gentry. They were enthusiastic and so was the chairman of the hospital board. "It is the only thing to do," the chairman agreed. "Can you move beds over there tonight?"

Throughout the remaining hours of that night we worked by the pale light of the setting moon, and when daylight came, we had set up forty beds in the powder magazine. A Red Cross flag fluttered over the entrance. The same little gateman was reinstated, wearing a white uniform. The ponderous key no longer hung in his inside pocket, but was stored with other valuables in the vault of the Hsiangya Hospital. We took the rifles and bayonets there, too, to hold them until the commanding general should requisition them.

That evening the Chinese secretary of the hospital wrote an official letter in my name, with all sorts of classical flourishes, to reach the new governor the following day. He would take office, we understood, at noon. We set the whole episode of the powder magazine before him as if we were military fellow strategists:

You will be pleased that we have eliminated a serious danger spot outside the north gate. Standing in the midst of a group of schools, near a college, and far too near the chief hospital of the city, the powder magazine there has imperiled life and property to so serious an extent that, with the approval of the acting mayor and the city fathers, we managed to get all the powder out yesterday afternoon and dumped it in the moat.

The north suburb is now quite safe from the danger of an explosion. The whole region round about knows you are giving approval. Furthermore, with the imminence of severe fighting, we suggest that your troops look to our hospital as the center where major injuries can be taken care of and your officers' ailments treated. As there will be need for a special ward for injured soldiers, we have moved beds and nurses to start such a ward in the old powder magazine. We need six hundred dollars at once to complete the equipment and know you will wish to provide the sum. As soon as we receive the subscription from you we shall put the ward fully in order and shall ask you to honor it by a visit later in the week.

The six hundred dollars arrived by special messenger the very next afternoon.

Later that week this new governor attended the opening ceremony of the new Hsiangya Hospital Annex. He made a flowery speech in praise of modern medicine, saying that in his own province he always called in a foreign doctor if one could be found. He congratulated the province—in which he was presently to prove himself a cruel, sadistic dictator—on having in its capital such a medical center, "where human charity may ever be demonstrated, and professional service provided." He assured us that he was glad that a powder magazine had so readily been converted into a benign and health-restoring unit for the service of society, and ended by pledging that the annual subsidy from the province for the Hsiangya medical work would never fail of payment so long as he was governor. We had occasion to remind him of his promise more than once.

XXXI

"YOU ARE TO BE SHOT
AT DAWN"

防民之口
甚於防川

To stop the mouth of the people
Is more difficult than to dam a river.

WITH the death of Dr. Sun Yat-sen in 1925 the ten desolate
years of strife among the self-seeking war lords drew to an
end. I was in Peking that spring during the three weeks after
Dr. Sun's death and found the atmosphere already charged
with a new impulse. The man who had dreamed and written
about democracy, the man who had stirred the Chinese resi-
dents of America and Europe and the South Sea Islands
to help introduce democratic government into their own home-
land, the man cynics called an idealist, had suddenly become
a legend. Now he was a source of strength for the whole nation. The Manchurian war lord felt it, the feudal leaders all
through China knew it. The restless decade was ending. Sun

Yat-sen had become, overnight, the inspiration of China.

Throughout these years of revolution the students had been the leaders in insisting on a democratic form of government. It was they who had led the revolt of 1919, against the decision at Versailles to turn Shantung province over to Japan. It was students who had hurried to the Ministry of Foreign Affairs in Peking to harangue and threaten the minister about a decision that seemed to them inimical to the sovereignty of China. Now, since the death of their great leader, they wondered whether their hopes for a true democracy would fade away. Leaders of thought in America and Britain, they knew, were beginning to speak sarcastically about the "democratization" of China.

There were student unions everywhere, but few with creative leadership. They grew fond of shouting, "Down with imperialism! Down with British imperialism!" The Chinese Communist Party was making many unpleasant comments about the British, and already there had been violent outbursts in Hong Kong.

The Shanghai Incident in May of that year, when shots were fired by the municipal police that killed several Chinese students going to a mass meeting, set all China ablaze. In every school and university the student unions demanded that "the foreigner" and his "imperialism" be driven out. My first knowledge of the student reaction in Changsha was brought to me by one of our most prominent young seniors, the daughter of Dr. Yen.

"May I have a private interview with you?" she asked. "It is very important."

She was a charming girl, one of the most gifted students on the campus. After doing college work in America she was now back in China for a year at Yali College. Her graduation was less than two weeks off.

In my office she poured out her story excitedly, although troubled to have to tell it so bluntly. "The entire student body of the academic college joined a city-wide student procession this morning, all except the medical college students who did not wish to be involved."

They had marched down to the big athletic field in front of the Hunan Educational Building, she told me, carrying banners with inscriptions denouncing all Westerners. In their speeches the students berated the British unmercifully. When the chairman asked what action the Student Union wished to take, there was great confusion—some shouting for one sort of penalty, some for another.

Finally, it was moved, seconded, and carried by acclamation that all foreigners in Changsha should be brought to the execution ground and shot at dawn on the following day.

"You are Number One on the list," the girl concluded. This doubtful honor was probably accorded to me because since 1923 I had been president of both the colleges, academic as well as medical. With a mixture of apprehension and amusement I asked, "Who is Number Two?"

"The academic dean, but, as you are president, they thought you should be shot first."

She assured me that of course neither she nor any of the other seniors, nor, for that matter, anyone in the entire institution, had any grudge against me personally or against any other of the faculty. She had felt it her duty to tell me about the vote of the city Student Union.

As soon as she left I called together the college and high-school deans, also Dr. Yen from the medical college. His was sure to be the voice we would heed. Presently we assembled all the heads of department and had a brief faculty executive session. A plan of action was promptly laid out.

Back in my house, I took up the telephone and called the number of the governor's yamen. Almost instantly a voice replied. "I am Governor Chao." It was unusual for a high official to answer an outside call.

In a few sentences I laid the situation before him. He knew, of course, about the mass meeting held by the Student Union, but had not learned that we were involved.

"This is serious," he said slowly, weighing each word, "but it is not a cause for anxiety. I will send a company of armed troops out to you at once." He asked that the members of the faculty go on duty also, and suggested that they divide by twos and stay on guard from then on through the night. If there was no disturbance by morning, we could be assured that the student storm had blown over.

That afternoon we watched a procession of students from the city schools parading to the river's edge, just west of our campus, carrying their banners with slogans that vowed vengeance on "all the imperialist nations." There was much shouting and reviling. The college gateman reported that, as they passed our gate, one student had shouted to him that the entire Student Union would make an attack on our campus after nightfall.

For ourselves, we followed the governor's instructions to the letter. Throughout the night we stood guard in two-hour watches and did not know until morning that the sight of the governor's soldiers at the gates had persuaded the students to lift our sentence of death.

All the next forenoon sedan chairs poured into the campus, each one bringing an irate father in a long silk gown. Frank words of paternal reprimand were heard all over our grounds.

"What did I send you to this school for?" we heard one father say. "I chose the most expensive school in Changsha for you, and hoped you would soon become a teacher of chemistry in the Government Normal School outside the South Gate. Now you have lost your chance for a modern education and, what is more, you have brought our whole family under suspicion. Do you think Governor Chao will give me the post that he had virtually promised?"

There were many downcast faces among the students all that day. But there was no rioting!

Nor was there any disturbance on graduation day a week later. As I handed out the college diplomas I caught the eye of the attractive young senior who had brought me the news of possible trouble. As she bowed and received her diploma, there was just the suggestion of a smile on her face.

It was our fifth commencement. I couldn't help thinking back to the distinguished gathering that had assembled in the college chapel in 1921, when the first graduates of the Hsiangya Medical College received their degrees and when diplomas were presented to the graduates of the school of nursing. It was then, too, that the bachelor's degree had been conferred on the first graduates of the Yali College of Arts and Science. On that occasion we had seen the fruition of fifteen years of ceaseless effort, and were convinced that the first two conditions laid down, nine years earlier, by the donor of the hospital had now been fully met. Everyone in China knew that the name Hsiangya stood for co-operation in medical education.

These new young doctors of medicine and graduate nurses, as well as the bachelors of arts, who were now filing slowly out of the chapel in their academic robes, were, like those who had graduated in the four preceding years, symbolic of the greater numbers who would follow. They would lead their people across the chasm between empirical and experimental science. It would be a slow process to establish experimental medicine in China, but these young medical graduates, who had a great sense of social responsibility, would help to erect a new system of medicine which would provide treatment and preventive care for all the people of China.

XXXII

"IF YOU PLANT FOR A HUNDRED YEARS"

If you plant for a year, plant grain;
If you plant for ten years, plant trees;
If you plant for a hundred years, plant men.

DURING the following year no fighting armies clashed in Hunan, but there were roving bands of guerrillas making trouble along the northern boundaries of the province. Canton, in contrast, where the revolutionary spirit of China had been centered, was tense with political excitement and military preparation. General Chiang Kai-shek was building a new revolutionary army to replace the mercenary forces of the old war lords. In the summer of 1926, a year after the student riots, General Chiang led his army northward, entered Hunan province, and advanced toward Changsha along the same route that had been followed by the Taiping Rebels seventy-five years earlier. When his troops reached the city they rested while scouts went ahead to make sure that the railway line was cleared of bandit ambuscades. They were hurrying to Wuchang to celebrate there, on October 10, the fifteenth anniversary of the outbreak of the revolution in that city.

To our delight we learned that one of the most conspicuous figures in the expeditionary force was our old friend, former Governor T'an Yen-k'ai, who had taken refuge in our house in 1917. Then I had told him that Hunan would count on his return. Now the whole populace turned out to welcome him. We were proud that, as the army came into the Hsiang River valley on its way to the central cities on the Long River, he had been the one man who was able to keep peace in the army. His knowledge of human nature, his tolerance and power to reconcile striving men, had made him Chiang's most trusted counselor.

As soon as they were settled T'an took the generals to visit the Hsiangya Hospital and the medical college. A few days later the hospital received a call to send a doctor to military headquarters at once. General Chiang Kai-shek was suffering from a toothache. The doctor responded at once.

There was the usual waiting in the reception room while word went to the chief. Uniformed officers were in and out of the room, stopping to study the military maps with which all the walls were hung. These were a different sort of decoration from those on the walls of the reception room at old Governor Nieh's house, a score of years earlier.

The doctor sipped tea and made conversation with a lieutenant, inquiring about the journey and the weather on the way up from Canton. Presently a brisk youngish man, in shirt sleeves and with his collar unfastened, came up to the table. The doctor greeted him with the usual "What is your honorable name, sir?"

"Chiang," was the brusque reply. The bystanders were amused at the doctor's failure to recognize the general.

No time was lost in examining the mouth. The old days of the deliberate examining of the pulse had vanished. This military man wanted action, not formality. The offending tooth was quickly drawn, and the patient was grateful at once. T'an Yen-k'ai came in just then and the conversation turned to the progress of the medical college.

"We shall count on you, sir, to become a patron of our medical work," the doctor said to the general. "Wherever you set up your quarters after you leave Changsha, we hope you will let us serve you medically." He added that the name Hsiangya meant co-operation between Chinese and Americans. The Americans had always wanted the medical college and hospital to be completely Chinese institutions. They had put up only the scaffolding of the structure.

"I am glad to hear you say that," replied the general. "We are grateful for everything you Westerners have done to help China, but we shall not stand for any more foreign imperialism." Just as soon as the national government was well organized at Nanking, he hoped that the Ministry of Education would select a group of the medical colleges and nationalize them. If this institution were chosen, he asked, would the board of managers agree to change the name to the National Hsiangya Medical College?

"That is the direction," said the American doctor, "in which both the Chinese and American members of the board hope to move." He explained that the American donor of the hospital had stipulated, when he made his gift, that the Chinese should think of it and support it as their own institution.

From that day forward Chiang Kai-shek worked steadily for Hsiangya. Within a few years the Ministry of Education designated the medical college as a national institution. Hunan educational leaders were now to contribute to the national government a gift more significant than their ancient provincial tribute of cinnabar.

This visit with T'an, who had shared our early struggles to build up the Hsiangya enterprise and had personally done so much to make our accomplishment possible, marked a milestone on our medical road.

Late in the summer of that year I resigned from my administrative posts in China. The announcement was noted in the Changsha papers with editorial approval:

> Educators in Changsha are grateful that Dr. Hume has based his resignation on the expectation that his tasks will be carried forward by Chinese administrators, who are now thoroughly trained and competent.

From the very beginning it had been my purpose to withdraw in this way. In fact, all the Americans on the staff conceived of their tasks as temporary. We planned to turn the leadership over to our Chinese colleagues as soon as they were ready.

The manner of our departure from the campus was unusual. The procession that escorted us to the railway station at Changsha North wound through the dried fields like a giant dragon, preceded by two men carrying long bamboo poles wound with double strings of firecrackers, ten thousand tiny crackers to a string, interspaced with giant crackers that punctuated the gentler rat-tat-tat with loud explosions.

The governor's deputy at the station brought word that the governor had ordered a private compartment reserved for us; but when the train drew in, all available space was taken by troops hurrying north to fight the roving bands of guerrillas. There was nothing to do except travel in the baggage car. We scrambled in, but there wasn't an inch of room there. At the mail clerk's suggestion, we spread out our bedding on top of the mail sacks.

Early in the morning the train waited over an hour at a siding. The conductor told us, quite calmly, that a bandit ambush had been discovered in hiding some miles ahead, and that we should have to wait until an armored car could arrive and be attached in front of the engine. When we finally reached Wuchang, a hundred soldiers, fully armed, poured out of that car. We had been well guarded.

The last person to bid us goodbye as we climbed in at the Changsha station had been our friendly old ricksha man who had been with us ever since we established the old hospital on West Archway Street. It was he who, when a boy of fifteen up from the country, had wandered into the hospital out of curiosity. He had passed Chou, the gateman, and had hidden behind the front door, hugging his little bundle. I was the first foreigner he had ever seen, and for years afterward he remembered how afraid he was of me. "Then I heard you say, 'T'ou Sz-fu, go down the corridor and catch that thief. I saw him hiding behind the door. He has a bundle under his arm.' I was frightened nearly to death."

But when T'ou Sz-fu, the orderly, looked behind the door, he found no thief, only a trembling boy from his own home village. From that day the boy belonged to the hospital. He had done so well as an apprentice that he was made a messenger. He had taken letters to the post office every day at five and, later on, helped to carry the sedan chair when I made medical calls, often late at night. Finally he had become the senior hospital ricksha man. He had been with us through riots and celebrations, at the opening of the Hsiangya Medical College, at the laying of the cornerstone of the new hospital, and at the graduation of our first doctors. For thirty years he had shared our discouragements and our triumphs.

It was he who had first told me the old Chinese proverb about planting men. How well he had known seedtime and harvest! They had been the familiar cycles of his boyhood, and he knew about the plow and the harrow, about fertilizing and planting. When he came to work at the hospital he had discovered that we, too, were meeting recurring cycles of adversity and happiness, of rocks and stumps to be cleared away, of furrows where the plow moved easily.

As the train left Changsha I thought of the young doctors, Hsiangya's first graduates. I was sure that, before long, they would be planting for a century.

After a few years I was asked to return to China to work toward getting other American-founded institutions to co-ordinate their work with the health plans of local Chinese leaders and the larger projects of the National Health Administration. It was this co-ordination that had been so successful in Hsiangya. On our way to Changsha we passed Yochow, and I could see from the train that same stone arch over the highway into Hunan which had stood like a forbidding sentry thirty years earlier. The bricks and stones with which the old gentry had blocked the arch had fallen out and lay beside the road, crumbling.

At Changsha East Station, standing by a modern motorcar, was our old ricksha man, dressed in a trim, new, hospital uniform. "What has become of the city walls?" I asked, looking for the familiar landmarks. They were gone and with them the

"Red-haired General." Where they had been was now a broad boulevard for the new motorcars.

The ricksha man told me what a stupendous job it had been to take down that old wall, whose foundations had been laid two thousand years earlier. "The doctors say," he went on, "that it has already made a great difference to the health of the city, especially in those narrow alleys just at the base of the wall."

Presently we reached the familiar buildings, but now there were so many more of them. Opposite the hospital stood the new provincial health center, with a roof of blue glazed tiles, as trim and as gracious in its lines as any classical Chinese temple of the old days. The only difference was that the old Confucian temples had shining yellow tiles like the roofs of the imperial palaces in old Peking.

One afternoon the ricksha man took me in town for dinner with Governor Ho. On the way to the yamen I stopped off to visit the school of nursing. It was a startling sight that greeted me when the dean opened the door of the assembly hall. A hundred students, *all girls*, rose and bowed. Only twenty years previously, I reminded them, Miss Gage had announced the opening of the school, coining the term for nurse, "Scholars to Watch and Guard." I remembered how timid the first girl students had been about registering.

On the way back, later that evening, the ricksha man stopped for a moment at the south gate of the hospital compound. With a sweep of the hand he pointed up through the darkness to where a hundred lights gleamed, like stars in the night, shining out from windows in the hospital and medical college, in the nursing school and the laboratories. "Look!" he said. "From such small seeds, planted only a little time ago, how great a harvest has grown!"

My assignment took me to nearly all the provinces, and in

every town I visited, I marveled at the progress made in so short a time. To my delight, the director of the National Health Administration invited me to inspect areas where newly established provincial and county health units were beginning to function. In one village I found a schoolboy of about twelve on a ladder before a slab of slate embedded in the wall of a house. In neat letters he was writing at the top of the upright columns, "VILLAGE NEWS, COUNTY NEWS, HEALTH NEWS." This was the village newspaper. Ten years, even five years earlier, no Chinese village would have had the slightest interest in daily bulletins about national affairs or health.

In another village I saw schoolchildren playing at recess, wearing arm bands marked, "FIRE SQUAD," "HEALTH SQUAD," and other such names. Everywhere China was becoming health conscious.

Most satisfying of all were the visits to the work of our Hsiangya graduates. Dr. Wu was in charge of the central tuberculosis hospital at the capital, and had elaborated a program for tuberculosis control which the government hoped soon to put into operation throughout China. Dr. Yao was health commissioner of Kweichow province and had made a survey, noting the counties in which malaria and dysentery were prevalent, as well as the breeding places of the different kinds of mosquitoes. Dr. Jen, Dr. Kao, and Dr. Ying were teaching a new generation of medical students in Shanghai.

It was a good harvest.

EPILOGUE

The way is one,
The winds blow together

When war came to China, Japanese armies overran Hunan, and Changsha, "the unconquerable city," fell into the hands of the enemy. The beloved hospital was occupied. Everywhere bricks and mortar crumbled, but our work lived on, immune to destruction.

We had seen the early beginnings in the Central Inn, and had experienced riots, revolution, and civil war. Those struggles were China's travail, as she gave birth to a new way of life. In these latter years, the ruthless foe, jealous of China's increasing power and unity, had invaded the land and threatened every constructive program.

The Hsiangya faculty and student body of two hundred and sixteen, eighty-eight of them girls, started westward when the enemy approached Changsha. They crossed rivers in boats when bridges had been burned or washed away. When streams were too shallow for boats, they waded, carrying packs of such books and equipment as they had been able to salvage. Now and then, when they stopped to rest, one of the faculty gave a lecture.

Finally they reached Kweiyang and settled in old temples or in crude mud huts whose thatched roofs they themselves helped to put on. Now they understood the old Chinese rhyme that said of Kweichow province:

276

Heaven: Never three days fully clear,
Earth: Nowhere three feet level here,
Man: None with three taels silver near.

The refugee students were put to it to get food and shelter. Some of the classes were held in the open at first, with mud bricks piled up for desks. At night the students studied by candlelight, later by the light of kerosene lamps. They smiled to think that they were carrying on the tradition of the old scholar, Ch'ê Yün, who, having no oil for his lamp when he was a boy, went into the summer darkness, caught hundreds of fireflies, and mastered the classics by their light.

The Hsiangya Medical College had the distinction of being the first in China that was asked to organize a hospital unit for the fighting front. It was sent to a post out on the Burma Road, near the Salween River, where men were still carving the roadway out of rocky mountainsides by the light of torches made of straw soaked in oil.

We were proud of the war record of the Hsiangya graduates in every part of China. It was Dr. Chang, principal of the medical college, who so courageously led that gallant trek to Kweiyang and, six years later, took the group on to Chungking. The students walked the entire distance, six hundred miles. Dr. T'ang made plague vaccine for the government in an old temple set in a grove of ancient cryptomeria and gingko trees. Dr. Hsiao stuck to his post as superintendent of the Hsiangya Hospital in the face of the Japanese attack, and opened three branch hospitals, east, west, and south, to keep the institution's influence vigorous during wartime.

Throughout the whole period of the war we kept asking ourselves, will the Hsiangya enterprise escape dissolution? We knew full well that it would survive if China survived. When we asked whether China would survive, we knew, long before her victory, that she would live on. Her history stretched back four thousand years.

Although attacked by land and sea, although her cities and coasts were blockaded and bombed, China lives on, inexhaustible and imperishable, as she has in the face of every previous foe. Her roots held firm because they were hidden deep in a soil that would never yield. The inner life of her people was knit into an organic vitality strong enough to defy destruction.

Now that victory has come to China, her doctors are already renewing the quest for added knowledge. Confident in the inheritance of a treasured past, and alert to new patterns of health and social welfare for their nation, they are even now eagerly forging links of the spirit between East and West.

Only those can enter effectively into her life who approach China's citadel by the way of friendship.

SALT OF THE EARTH